SCHOLASTIC

100 MATHS ASSESSMENT LESSONS

TERMS AND CONDITIONS

IMPORTANT - PERMITTED USE AND WARNINGS - READ CAREFULLY BEFORE USING

Licence

YEAR 6

Scottish Primary 7

Minimum specification:
- PC or Mac with a CD-ROM drive and 512 Mb RAM (recommended)
- Windows 98SE or above/Mac OSX.4 or above
- Recommended minimum processor speed: 1 GHz

For all technical support queries, please phone Scholastic Customer Services on 0845 603 9091.

John Davis, Sonia Tibbatts and Julie Dyer

CREDITS

Authors
John Davis, Sonia Tibbatts
and Julie Dyer

Series Consultant
Ann Montague-Smith

Development Editor
Kate Baxter

Editors
Mary Nathan and
Christine Vaughan

Assistant Editor
Margaret Eaton

Series Designers
Joy Monkhouse, Micky Pledge
and Melissa Leeke

Designer
Quadrum Publishing Solutions

Illustrations
Garry Davies

CD-ROM development
CD-ROM developed in
association with Vivid
Interactive

Additional material
Transitional tests written by
Joan Nield and Lesley Fletcher

Mixed Sources
Product group from well-managed
forests and other controlled sources
www.fsc.org Cert no. TT-COC-002769
© 1996 Forest Stewardship Council

ACKNOWLEDGEMENTS

Extracts from the Primary National Strategy's *Primary Framework for Mathematics* (2006) www.standards.dfes.gov.uk/primaryframework and the Interactive Teaching Programs originally developed for the National Numeracy Strategy © Crown copyright. Reproduced under the terms of the Click Use Licence.

Every effort has been made to trace copyright holders for the works reproduced in this book, and the publishers apologise for any inadvertent omissions.

Published by Scholastic Ltd
Villiers House
Clarendon Avenue
Leamington Spa
Warwickshire CV32 5PR

www.scholastic.co.uk

Designed using Adobe InDesign.

Printed by Bell and Bain Ltd, Glasgow

1 2 3 4 5 6 7 8 9   9 0 1 2 3 4 5 6 7 8 9

Text © 2009 John Davis, Sonia Tibbatts and Julie Dyer

© 2009 Scholastic Ltd

British Library Cataloguing-in-Publication Data
A catalogue record for this book is available from the British Library.

ISBN 978-1407-10194-1

Contents

Introduction 4–6

Block A: Counting, partitioning and calculating 7
Unit 1 8–16
Unit 2 17–26
Unit 3 27–35
Periodic assessment 36
Periodic assessment photocopiables 37–38

Block B: Securing number facts, understanding shape 39
Unit 1 40–48
Unit 2 49–60
Unit 3 61–72
Periodic assessment 73
Periodic assessment photocopiables 74–76

Block C: Handling data and measures 77
Unit 1 78–85
Unit 2 86–95
Unit 3 96–105
Periodic assessment 106
Periodic assessment photocopiables 107–108

Block D: Calculating, measuring and understanding shape 109
Unit 1 110–121
Unit 2 122–133
Unit 3 134–145
Periodic assessment 146
Periodic assessment photocopiables 147–148

Block E: Securing number facts, relationships and calculating 149
Unit 1 150–161
Unit 2 162–171
Unit 3 172–184
Periodic assessment 185
Periodic assessment photocopiables 186–187

Transitional assessment 188–189

APP flow diagram 190

Individual pupil AF tracking sheet 191

100 Maths Assessment Lessons

About the series

100 Maths Assessment Lessons is designed to provide assessment opportunities for all children. Linked to the renewed *Primary Framework for Mathematics*, it also supports the implementation of the new *Assessing Pupil's Progress* (APP) guidelines by linking the new APP assessment focuses to the PNS Framework objectives. Each title in the series also provides single-level tests that can be used at the end of a year, or at any point throughout the year, to provide a summary of where, in relation to national standards, learners are at a given point in time. By using the titles in this series, a teacher or school can be sure that they are covering the mathematics curriculum and obtaining relevant data about their children's achievements.

About assessment

100 Maths Assessment Lessons provides a wide range of opportunities for teachers and children to assess progress. There are three different types of assessment identified by the APP guidelines:

Day to day

Day-to-day assessment is an integral and essential part of effective learning and teaching. Teachers and children continually reflect on how learning is progressing, see where improvements can be made and identify the next steps to take. Strategies that should be part of everyday learning and teaching include:
● sharing and talking about learning objectives, learning outcomes and success criteria with children
● observing and listening to gather intelligence
● planning for group talk, peer assessment and self-assessment to help children develop as independent learners.

Periodic assessment

The purpose of periodic assessment is to give an overview of progress and provide diagnostic information about the progress of individual children, linked to national standards. It is intended to be used at regular (half-termly or termly) intervals to provide an overview of performance based on a wide range of evidence. Periodic assessment should be used to:
● make a periodic review of progress and attainment across a whole task
● identify gaps in experience and inform planning
● help learners know and recognise the standards they are aiming for
● involve both learner and teacher in reviewing and reflecting on evidence.

Transitional assessment

Transitional assessment should be used at points of transition which might be from year to year, school to school or level to level. The pupils' progress data from day-to-day assessment and periodic assessment will support the teacher in making decisions about how pupils are likely to perform in transitional assessments. The key characteristics of transitional assessment are:
● it brings together evidence, including tests, to reach a view of attainment

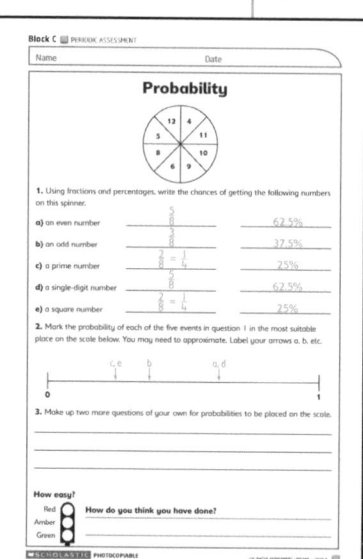

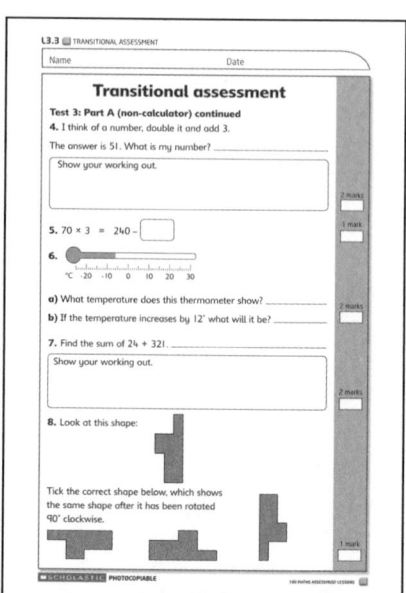

■SCHOLASTIC

- it is externally validated and externally communicated
- it is set within the framework of national standards.

For a complete list of strategies for day-to-day assessment and further information about periodic and transitional assessment, visit the National Strategies website (**http://nationalstrategies.standards.dcsf.gov.uk**).

About this book

This book is set out in the five blocks that form the renewed *Primary Framework for Mathematics*. Each block consists of three units, with each unit containing:
- an overview of the work covered in the unit, including the objectives, assessment focuses and learning outcomes for each activity (end-of-year objectives are denoted in bold text)
- day-to-day assessment activities based upon the assessment for learning and children's learning outcomes for each objective within a unit (note that the using and applying objectives are either incorporated into other assessments, or assessed on their own, depending upon the content and context of the unit)
- periodic assessment activities based on the end-of-year objectives within each unit.

Assessment activities

Each activity contains:
- details of children's expected prior learning before the activity is used
- the relevant objective(s) and vocabulary that children are expected to know
- description of the activity for the teacher or learning support assistant
- group, paired or individual work for the children. Where adult intervention is required, this is explained. Most of the activities include the use of an activity sheet or interactive activity from the CD-ROM
- clear differentiation, to support less confident learners in the group or to extend the learning for the more confident learners
- common misconceptions and how to remediate these
- probing questions to ask the children
- next steps: these are differentiated to help teachers decide how to help children who need further support. Suggestions for further work and references to related Framework units or blocks are given to support or extend the children.

What's on the CD-ROM?

Each CD-ROM contains a wealth of resources. These include:
- **worksheets** with answers, where appropriate, that can be toggled by clicking on the 'show' or 'hide' buttons at the bottom of the screen
- **transitional assessments:** year-appropriate single-level tests, oral tests, mark schemes and instructions
- **general resource sheets** (for example, number grids) designed to support a number of lessons
- **interactive activities:** for individuals or small groups, with in-built marking to assess specific objectives
- **Interactive Teaching Programs:** specific ITPs, originally developed for the National Numeracy Strategy
- **whiteboard tools:** a set of tools (including a pen, highlighter and eraser) that can be used to annotate activity sheets for whole-class lessons. These tools will work on any interactive whiteboard
- **display pages:** some activities require a problem or investigation to be shown to the whole class on an interactive whiteboard. The whiteboard tools can also be used with these images to annotate them as necessary
- **editable planning grids** (in Word format) are available to help teachers integrate the lessons into their planning.

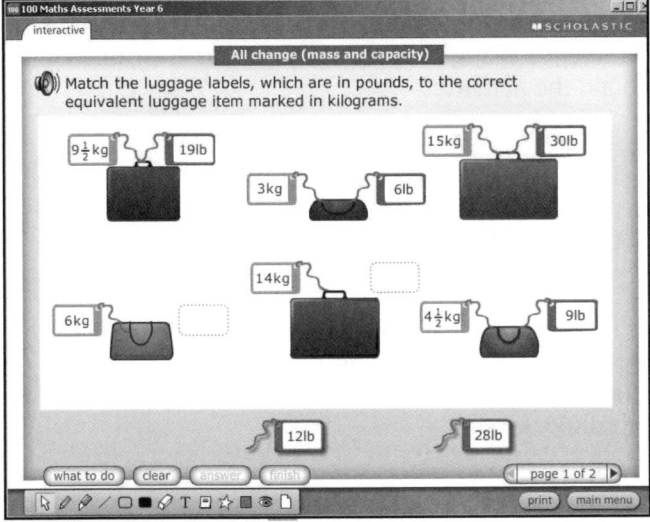

How to use the CD-ROM

System requirements
Minimum specification:
- PC or Mac with a CD-ROM drive and 512 Mb RAM (recommended)
- Windows 98SE or above/Mac OS X.4 or above
- Recommended minimum processor speed: 1 GHz

Getting started
The *100 Maths Assessment Lessons* CD-ROM should auto run when inserted into your CD drive. If it does not, browse to your CD drive to view the contents of the CD-ROM and click on the *100 Maths Assessment Lessons* icon.

From the start-up screen you will find four options: select **Credits** to view a list of acknowledgements. Click on **Register** to register the product in order to receive product updates and special offers. Click on **How to use this CD-ROM** to access support notes for using the CD-ROM. Finally, if you agree to the terms and conditions, select **Start** to move to the main menu.

For all technical support queries, contact Scholastic Customer Services help desk on 0845 6039091.

How to use the materials
The materials contained in the book and on the CD-ROM can be used with one child, a group, or in a whole-class activity. Decide who is ready to be assessed from the daily work that the children complete and from your observations. The CD-ROM allows users to search for resources by block, unit or lesson. Users can also search by Framework objective, assessment focus or by resource type (for example, worksheet, interactive resource, display page or ITP).

Day-to-day assessments
These should be used to support learning. They can be used during a lesson, when you judge that children are ready for an assessment activity. The materials can also be used weekly or after a unit of work has been completed.

Periodic assessments
These can be used with a group of children rather than with the whole class. This could be at the end of a unit of work (for example, at the end of a half-term or term). Decide who is ready to be assessed using the outcomes of the day-to-day assessment activities and your observations of children's performance.

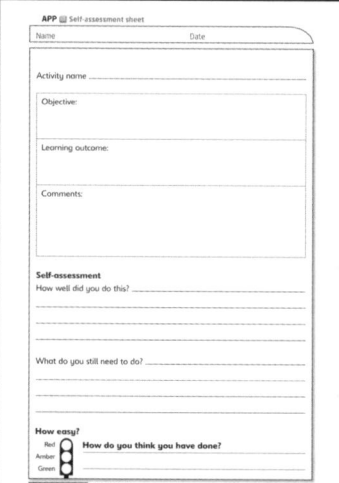

Self-assessment
A self-assessment sheet is provided for you and the children to complete. It can be used where there is no activity sheet, so that there is evidence of the children's confidence in what they have learned and how well they can use that learning. There are 'traffic lights' at the bottom of the sheet that children can shade to show their confidence: red for 'need help'; orange for 'having some understanding'; green for 'go!' (ie the child feels confident with his/her learning).

All the activity sheets also have the traffic light system for the children to record their level of confidence, along with a space for them to write about how easy/hard they found the activity.

Transitional tests
These tests provide evidence of where, in relation to national standards, children are at a given point in time. Photocopiable tests (both written and oral), mark schemes and answer sheets are all available on the CD-ROM.

Class PET
A whole-school version of *100 Maths Assessment Lessons* is available with an expanded range of digital assessment activities, as well as the facility to report, record and track pupil's work. For further information visit the Class PET website, **www.scholastic.co.uk/classpet**.

BLOCK A
Counting, partitioning and calculating

Expected prior learning
Check that children can already:
- explain reasoning using text, diagrams and symbols
- solve one- and two-step problems involving whole numbers and decimals and all four operations, choosing and using appropriate calculation strategies
- order positive and negative numbers in context
- explain what each digit represents in whole numbers and decimals with corresponding division facts
- use mental methods to find sums, differences, doubles and halves of decimals (eg 6.5 + 2.7, halve 5.6, double 0.34), to multiply a two-digit by a one-digit number, to multiply by 25 and to subtract one near multiple of 1000 from another (eg 6070 - 4097)
- use efficient written methods to add and subtract whole numbers and decimals with up to two places, to multiply HTU × U, TU × TU and U.t × U, and to divide HTU ÷ U
- use a calculator to solve problems, interpreting the display correctly
- use rounding and inverse operations to estimate and check calculations.

Objectives overview
The text in this diagram identifies the focus of mathematics learning within the block.

Key aspects of learning
- Social skills
- Problem solving
- Communication

Solving multi-step word problems involving numbers, money or measures

Ordering, partitioning and rounding decimals to three places; +ve and –ve integers

Explaining reasoning and conclusions, orally and on paper, using words, diagrams, symbols

**BLOCK A:
Counting,
partitioning and
calculating**

Addition and subtraction

Mental calculations

Efficient written methods: whole numbers and decimals

Multiplication and division

Mental methods: TU × U, TU/U and special cases

Written methods: TU × TU, HTU × TU, HTU/U, multiplying and dividing decimals by a one-digit integer

Using a calculator

Unit 1 □ Counting, partitioning and calculating

Introduction

This eight-lesson block gives prominence to using and applying mathematics where children work with number sequences. They are encouraged to explain how sequences are formed and predict how they will progress. Children investigate positive and negative numbers in practical settings such as reading temperatures. They strengthen their understanding of decimal notation in both written form and mentally. There are also activities in which they use their knowledge of place value and multiplication facts to solve multiplication and division problems including decimals.

Framework objectives	Assessment focuses		Success criteria for Year 6	Learning outcomes
	Level 5	Level 4		
① In sequence				
Explain reasoning and conclusions, using words, symbols or diagrams as appropriate	• draw simple conclusions of their own and give an explanation of their reasoning, e.g. • explain and justify their methods and solution • identify more complex patterns, making generalisations in words and begin to express generalisations using symbolic notation • use examples and counter-examples to justify conclusions	• search for a solution by trying out ideas of their own, e.g. • check their methods and justify answers • identify patterns as they work and form their own generalisations/rules in words	• can continue a sequence of numbers • can describe a number sequence • can generate a number sequence • can explain reasoning when working with number sequences	*I can say whether a number will occur in a sequence, explaining my reasoning.*
② Fairground ride				
Find the difference between a positive and a negative integer, or two negative integers, in context	• add and subtract negative numbers in context • solve simple problems involving ordering, adding, subtracting negative numbers in context	• solve problems with or without a calculator, e.g. • carry out simple calculations involving negative numbers in context	• can find the difference between positive and negative numbers • can work with positive/negative numbers in context, e.g. temperature	*I can find the difference between positive and negative integers.*
③ Decimal rings ④ All in order				
Use decimal notation for tenths, hundredths and thousandths; partition, round and order decimals with up to three places, and position them on the number line	• use equivalence between fractions, e.g. • convert fractions such as 2/5 into tenths or hundredths and express them as decimals or percentages and vice versa • round decimals to the nearest decimal place • order fractions and decimals, e.g. • order decimals that have a mixture of one, two or three decimal places	• recognise approximate proportions of a whole and use simple fractions and percentages to describe these, e.g. • recognise simple equivalence between fractions, decimals and percentages, e.g. 1/2, 1/4, 1/10, 3/4 • order decimals to three decimal places	• knows the place value of numbers to three decimal places • can order decimal numbers • knows the position of decimal numbers on a number line • can round decimal numbers	*I can round large numbers to the nearest multiple of 10, 100 or 1000.*

Unit 1 📖 Counting, partitioning and calculating

Framework objectives	Assessment focuses		Success criteria for Year 6	Learning outcomes
	Level 5	Level 4		
⑤ Find me				
Use knowledge of place value and multiplication facts to 10 × 10 to derive related multiplication and division facts involving decimals (e.g. 0.8 × 7, 4.8 ÷ 6)	• use all four operations with decimals to two places, e.g. ◦ multiply or divide decimal numbers by a single digit, e.g. 31.62 × 7	• multiply a simple decimal by a single digit, e.g. ◦ calculate 36.2 × 8 • quickly derive division facts that correspond to multiplication facts up to 10 × 10	• knows multiplication facts up to 10 × 10 • can use this knowledge to work out other number facts including decimals • knows and is able to work with corresponding division facts	*I can use table facts to work out other facts with decimals.*
⑥ Wipe out				
Calculate mentally with integers and decimals: U.t ± U.t, TU × U, TU ÷ U, U.t × U, U.t ÷ U	• use all four operations with decimals to two places, e.g. ◦ add and subtract numbers that do not have the same number of decimal places ◦ multiply or divide decimal numbers by a single digit, e.g. 31.62 × 7	• use a range of mental methods of computation with all operations, e.g. ◦ calculate complements to 1000 • recall multiplication facts up to 10 × 10 and quickly derive corresponding division facts, e.g. ◦ use their knowledge of tables and place value in calculations with multiples of 10 such as 30 × 7, 180 ÷ 3	• can add, subtract, multiply and divide whole numbers and decimals mentally • can provide appropriate questions when given an answer • can explain methods used to find answers mentally	*I can add, subtract, multiply and divide whole numbers and decimals in my head.*
⑦ Bargain time				
Use a calculator to solve problems involving multi-step calculations	• use a calculator where appropriate to calculate fractions/percentages of quantities/measurements, e.g. ◦ find fractions of quantities such as 3/8 of 980 ◦ find percentages such as 15% of 360g	• use inverse operations, e.g. ◦ use a calculator and inverse operations to find missing numbers, including decimals • solve problems with or without a calculator	• knows when to use a calculator to work out calculations • can use a calculator when more than one step is needed to solve a problem • can solve percentage problems using a calculator	*I can use a calculator to solve problems with more than one step.*
⑧ Ticket sales				
Use approximations, inverse operations and tests of divisibility to estimate and check results	• approximate to check answers to problems are of the correct magnitude • check solutions by applying inverse operations or estimating using approximations • check results, considering whether these are reasonable, e.g. ◦ check as they work, spotting and correcting errors and reviewing methods	• check the reasonableness of results with reference to the context or size of numbers • develop own strategies for solving problems, e.g. ◦ check answers and ensure solutions make sense in the context of the problem ◦ review their work and approaches	• knows approximately what an answer will be before doing a calculation • can check answers make sense in the context of the problem	*I can estimate and check the calculations that I do.*

Activity ①

Prior learning
Children can fill in the gaps in a given sequence of numbers. They can predict how a number sequence will continue, given the start.

Framework objective
Explain reasoning and conclusions, using words, symbols or diagrams as appropriate

Vocabulary
problem, solution, answer, strategy, explain, reason, predict, relationship, rule, formula, sequence, term, consecutive

Resources
Worksheet: In sequence

① In sequence

Provide each child with a copy of the worksheet 'In sequence'. Ask the children to complete the number sequences and explain how they obtained the solutions.

Teacher support
Less confident learners: Support these children with adding on fractions and decimals. Ensure that they are aware that some involve two-step sequences (for example, +3, +5).
More confident learners: Quickly move these children on to two-step sequences and sequences using fractions and decimals.

Common misconceptions
Children do not recognise the pattern in the part of the sequence already given. Ask the children to mark the actual differences in the space between the numbers in the sequence. Emphasise working from the known to the unknown.

Probing questions
● How many numbers need to be given before a regular pattern can be established?
● Can number sequences still work successfully when numbers decrease rather than increase in size?

Next steps
Support: Provide further practice for children to try out two-step patterns and also their own simple versions using fractions and decimals. Refer back to Year 5 Block E Unit 3.
Extension: Encourage children to investigate other number sequences such as square or triangular numbers and the Fibonacci series. Refer also to Year 6 Block E Unit 1.

Activity ②

Prior learning Children can explain how a positive/negative number line works and find the difference between positive and negative integers in context, for example a thermometer.	**Framework objective** Find the difference between a positive and negative integer, or two negative integers, in context **Vocabulary** numeral, integer, positive, negative, order, ascending, descending **Resources** **Interactive activity:** Fairground ride **Worksheet:** Fairground ride **Classroom resources:** individual whiteboards and pens

② Fairground ride

Show the class the interactive activity 'Fairground ride'. In this activity, the children are encouraged to add positive and negative numbers using mental arithmetic.

Teacher support

Less confident learners: Encourage these children to use jottings to work out the answers for themselves before class discussion. You can give extra support by providing them with copies of the worksheet 'Fairground ride'.
More confident learners: Ask these children to imagine that the ride went below -12 or -15 and set more detailed questions accordingly.

Common misconceptions

Children confuse the rules about finding the difference between a positive and a negative integer and two negative or two positive integers.
With a positive and negative integer, find the difference by adding the numbers (for example -5 to +3 is 8). With two positive or two negative integers, subtract the numbers, smaller from larger (for example +4 to +7 is 3 and -5 to -1 is 4).

Probing questions

● On which sides of the zero do positive and negative numbers always come on a number line?
● Can you think of any other situations where positive and negative numbers are used? (On a thermometer, in a lift.)

Next steps

Support: Some children may still need to use a number line so that they can count steps physically in order to find answers. Reinforce that moving in a positive direction means going to the right and moving in a negative direction means going to the left. Refer back to Year 5 Block E Unit 3.
Extension: Write down a pair of numbers from the number line and ask children to put the greater than or less than signs (< or >) between them. For example, -2 < 1 and 3 > -4. Refer also to Year 6 Block E Unit 1.

Activities ③ and ④

Prior learning
Children can use decimal notation to three decimal places and can round and order decimals and position them on a number line.

Framework objective
Use decimal notation for tenths, hundredths and thousandths; partition, round and order decimals with up to three decimal places and position them on a number line

Vocabulary
place value, digit, partition, decimal point, decimal place, tenths, hundredths, thousandths, round, order, position

Resources
Worksheets: Decimal rings, All in order

③ Decimal rings

Provide each child with a copy of the worksheet 'Decimal rings'. Ask the children to identify the place value of the ringed digits in decimal numbers and also place decimals on a number line.

Teacher support
Less confident learners: These children may still need the support of a place value chart with t, h and th placed over the columns used for decimal numbers.
More confident learners: Encourage these children to use three decimal places when recording – for example, 0.258km = 258m and 30g = 0.030kg.

Common misconceptions
Children remain confused about which numbers are whole numbers and which are decimal numbers.
Emphasise constantly that whole numbers come on the left-hand side of the decimal point and decimal numbers are on the right-hand side of the decimal point. Keep appropriate decimal place value charts on display.

Probing questions
● How should decimal numbers be correctly described? For example, 4.38 not as 4 point 38 but as 4 and $3/10$ and $8/100$ or as 4 and $38/100$.
● How is decimal notation used in the context of money? For example, £5.27 is £5 $27/100$.

Next steps
Support: Ensure that the children are confident with using numbers to one and two decimal places before extending this to three decimal places. Refer back to Year 5 Block E Unit 3.
Extension: Provide children with plenty of practical measuring activities around the school using decimal numbers to three decimal places wherever possible. Refer also to Year 6 Block A Units 2 and 3.

④ All in order

Provide each child with a copy of the worksheet 'All in order'. In this activity the children are asked to order sets of decimal numbers and to complete some rounding activities.

Teacher support
Less confident learners: Make sure these children are confident with numbers that only have one digit to the right of the decimal point before moving on.

More confident learners: Give these children plenty of examples of sorting decimal numbers in order, including those that have the same whole number but are written to two or three decimal numbers.

Common misconceptions
Children tend to look first at the size of certain digits rather than their position in relation to the decimal point.
Reinforce place value involving decimal numbers so that children are sure of the value of numbers in particular columns.

Probing questions
● What do you look for first when you order a set of decimal numbers?
● Which part of each number do you look at to help you?

Next steps
Support: Provide practical situations in which children have to sort decimal numbers into order. Say: *The standing jump distances of three children are 1.75m, 1.09m, 1.63m. Who jumps furthest?* Refer back to Year 5 Block E Unit 3.
Extension: Ask children to suggest a decimal fraction that lies between two numbers. Refer also to Year 6 Block A Units 2 and 3.

Activity ⑤

Prior learning
Children know their multiplication facts to 10 × 10. They can relate these facts to decimals numbers, for example if 8 × 3 = 24 then 8 × 0.3 = 2.4.

Framework objective
Use knowledge of place value and multiplication facts to 10 × 10 to derive related multiplication and division facts involving decimals (for example, 0.8 × 7, 4.8 ÷ 6)

Vocabulary
place value, digit, numeral, decimal point, decimal place, multiply, divide

Resources
Worksheet: Find me
Resource sheet: Multiplication square (for support)

⑤ Find me

Provide the children with copies of the worksheet 'Find me', in which they are asked to derive multiplication and division facts from the factors of 48.

Teacher support
Less confident learners: Provide these children with the resource sheet 'Multiplication square'. Remind them how to find the full list of factors of a number.
More confident learners: Encourage these children to start with larger numbers that have more factors, so extending the range of their investigation.

Common misconceptions
Children assume that both the numbers they are multiplying should contain decimal points (for example, if 8 × 3 = 24 then 0.8 × 0.3 = 2.4 instead of 0.8 × 3 = 2.4).
Provide calculators so that children can check quickly to see if they have decimal points in the correct positions.

Probing questions
● How can we make sure that all the factors of a number have been selected?

BLOCK A

- When solutions have been derived, how can we check that decimal points have been placed in the correct position?

Next steps
Support: Ensure that the children are confident with deriving simple multiplication decimal facts before moving on to consider division. Refer back to Year 5 Block A Unit 3.
Extension: Focus more on division facts starting with a decimal number (for example, 2.1 ÷ 7 = ? and 4.8 ÷ 6 = ?). Refer also to Year 6 Block B Units 1, 2 and 3.

Activity ⑥

Prior learning
Children can add, subtract, multiply and divide small whole numbers mentally. They understand what happens to the decimal point when decimal numbers are multiplied or divided.

Framework objective
Calculate mentally with integers and decimals: U.t ± U.t, TU × U, TU ÷ U, U.t × U, U.t ÷ U

Vocabulary
problem, solution, calculate, calculation, operation, answer, method, strategy, place value, numeral, digit, integer, decimal point, decimal place, add, subtract, multiply, divide

Resources
Display page: Wipe out
Resource sheets: Multiplication square, Self-assessment

⑥ Wipe out

Work with groups of four/five children for this oral assessment activity, using the 'Wipe out' display page. This on-screen page shows the answers to the 20 quick-fire oral questions below. Ask the questions in random order, so that the answers do not automatically follow the sequence shown on the display page.

6.5 + 3.5	20.3 – 14.6	64 × 3	96 ÷ 8
9.7 + 4.8	36.4 – 21.7	87 × 6	4.7 × 3
15.3 + 9.4	43.7 – 36.8	20 ÷ 4	9.8 × 5
24.9 + 8.7	30 × 4	72 ÷ 9	6.4 ÷ 8
15.5 – 10.2	27 × 5	75 ÷ 5	6.3 ÷ 9

Encourage the children to take it in turns to calculate answers mentally, say the answer out loud, then find it on the whiteboard display page and cross it out using the pen tool. Decide whether to use the self-assessment sheet for the children to record their achievements and what they need to do next.

Teacher support
Less confident learners: If necessary, simplify the decimal numbers in the questions and allow use of table squares as additional support.
More confident learners: Invite these children to devise their own quick-fire questions to try on others in the group.

Common misconceptions
Children calculate answers by removing the decimal point but then forget to insert it again in the answer (for example, they state that 6.5 + 3.5 = 100 instead of 10.0).
Encourage children to calculate the approximate answer first. For example, 24.9 + 8.7 is approximately 25 + 9 = 34, so the real answer is 33.6 not 3.36.

Probing questions
- Which is the most suitable method to use for each of the four rules?
- What is the best way of checking that the answer is correct?

Next steps
Support: Make some of the questions multiple choice to support the children's reasoning. Ask, for example: *Does 10.5 take away 4.9 equal 56, 5.6 or 6.5?*
Extension: Provide children with a solution and ask them to provide their own questions. For example: *Make up addition, subtraction, multiplication and division facts that have an answer of 1.6.* Refer also to Year 6 Block D Unit 1.

Activity ⑦

Prior learning
Children can carry out simple operations on the calculator and are aware that methods may change when two-step operations are involved. They can use one of the methods on the calculator to find percentages.

Framework objective
Use a calculator to solve problems involving multi-step calculations

Vocabulary
problem, solution, calculate, operation, answer, method, strategy, explain, reason, calculator, display, enter, clear, percentage, reduction, saving, sale price, change

Resources
Worksheet: Bargain time
Classroom resources: calculators

⑦ Bargain time

Provide each child with a copy of the worksheet 'Bargain time'. They each need a calculator and should be reminded that calculations will involve more than one step. They must calculate, for each item, how much is saved in the sale, the new purchase price of the article and how much change will need to be given.

Teacher support
Less confident learners: Support these children with at least one method of finding percentages using a calculator.
More confident learners: Ask children to explain to an adult and/or other children how they found the solutions They should discuss several methods if possible.

Common misconceptions
Children want to feed too many operations into the calculator at the same time. It may be necessary to use the = key or clear between stages in order to separate out operations. Discuss using the memory key, or ask the children to write down some of the stages if using the memory facility is not appropriate.

Probing questions
- Which keys needed to be pressed to find the correct solution?
- Could other keys have been used to make the calculation easier?

Next steps
Support: Revise with children the correct use of the % key on the calculator when carrying out problems of this kind. Refer back to Year 5 Block E Unit 3.
Extension: Let children use a calculator to find solutions to problems involving more than three steps. Ask them to experiment with other calculator functions, such as the % and square root signs. Refer also to Year 6 Block C Unit 2.

Activity ⑧

Prior learning
Children can round integers to the nearest 1, 100 and 1000 and round decimal numbers to the nearest whole number.

Framework objective
Use approximations, inverse operations and tests of divisibility to estimate and check results

Vocabulary
digit, numeral, integer, decimal points, decimal number, round, estimate, approximate, approximately, add, subtract, multiply, divide

Resources
Display page: Ticket sales
Worksheet: Ticket sales

⑧ Ticket sales

Reveal the display page 'Ticket sales'. Go through the questions on the screen with the children. Then provide each child with a copy of the corresponding worksheet to complete individually. Ask them to work out approximate answers and then to check to see how close they have been.

Teacher support
Less confident learners: Support these children with rounding numbers to the nearest 10, 100 and 1000 and with money to the nearest pound.
More confident learners: Expect these children to be precise in their rounding – for example, 419 rounded to 420 rather than 400 and £4.92 rounded to £4.90 rather than £5.

Common misconceptions
Children are reluctant to round numbers for approximating because they feel what they say will be a long way from the correct answer.
Encourage children to carry out approximations in all forms of calculation they do. They will become more skilled with greater practice.

Probing questions
● How do you know that your calculation is probably right?
● Which other ways could you check the answer to the calculation?

Next steps
Support: Encourage children to express calculations in more general terms before moving on to more precise approximations. For example, 523 + 228 is more than 500 + 200 and 605 – 197 is about 600 – 200. Refer back to Year 5 Block A Unit 1.
Extension: Introduce a points system based on how close each approximate answer was – for example, 10 points within 20, 5 points within 30, 1 point within 50. Refer to Year 6 Block D Unit 1.

Unit 2 Counting, partitioning and calculating

Introduction

More using and applying mathematics work opens this nine-lesson block, specifically finding missing numbers, including decimals. Children are required to explain orally how they obtained their answers. Solving 'real-life' word problems follows this. In the second part of the unit the focus switches to using written methods for the addition or subtraction of integers, multiplying a three-digit number by a two-digit number and dividing three-digit numbers by a single digit. The unit concludes with using approximation to estimate and check answers.

Framework objectives	Assessment focuses		Success criteria for Year 6	Learning outcomes
	Level 5	Level 4		
1 What am I?				
Explain reasoning and conclusions, using words, symbols or diagrams as appropriate	• draw simple conclusions of their own and give an explanation of their reasoning, e.g. • explain and justify their methods and solution • identify more complex patterns, making generalisations in words and begin to express generalisations using symbolic notation	• search for a solution by trying out ideas of their own, e.g. • check their methods and justify answers • identify patterns as they work and form their own generalisations/rules in words	• can find missing numbers by solving problems • can find the solution to a problem by trying several ideas • can explain methods of reasoning	*I can explain my reasoning and conclusions, using symbols to represent unknown numbers.*
2 Your choice				
Solve multi-step problems, and problems involving fractions, decimals and percentages; choose and use appropriate calculation strategies at each stage, including calculator use	• identify and obtain necessary information to carry through a task and solve mathematical problems	• develop own strategies for solving problems	• knows the meaning of key vocabulary used in problems • can use a coherent strategy in solving word problems • can describe the strategy used to find a solution • can check final results	*I can solve problems involving more than one step.*
3 Building bricks				
Use decimal notation for tenths, hundredths and thousandths; partition, round and order decimals with up to three places, and position them on the number line	• use equivalence between fractions, e.g. • convert fractions such as $2/5$ into tenths or hundredths and express them as decimals or percentages and vice versa • round decimals to the nearest decimal place • order fractions and decimals, e.g. • order decimals that have a mixture of one, two or three decimal places	• recognise approximate proportions of a whole and use simple fractions and percentages to describe these, e.g. • recognise simple equivalence between fractions, decimals and percentages, e.g. $1/2$, $1/4$, $1/10$, $3/4$ • order decimals to three decimal places	• can identify and order three-place decimals • rounds off decimals to the nearest whole number or nearest tenth	*I can use decimals with up to three places and order them on a number line. I can round decimals to the nearest whole number or the nearest tenth.*

Unit 2 ⬜ Counting, partitioning and calculating

Framework objectives	Assessment focuses		Success criteria for Year 6	Learning outcomes
	Level 5	Level 4		
④ **Partner time**				
Use knowledge of place value and multiplication facts to 10 × 10 to derive related multiplication and division facts involving decimals	● use all four operations with decimals to two places, e.g. ● multiply or divide decimal numbers by a single digit, e.g. 31.62 × 7	● multiply a simple decimal by a single digit, e.g. ● calculate 36.2 × 8 ● quickly derive division facts that correspond to multiplication facts up to 10 × 10	● knows multiplication facts to 10 × 10 ● can derive related decimal multiplication and division facts from these	*I can use table facts to work out other facts with decimals.*
⑤ **Beat the clock**				
Calculate mentally with integers and decimals: U.t ± U.t, TU × U, TU ÷ U, U.t × U, U.t ÷ U	● use all four operations with decimals to two places, e.g. ● add and subtract numbers that do not have the same number of decimal places ● multiply or divide decimal numbers by a single digit	● use a range of mental methods of computation with all operations ● recall multiplication facts up to 10 × 10 and quickly derive corresponding division facts	● can add, subtract, multiply and divide whole numbers and decimals mentally ● can use a range of mental computation methods ● describes and explains mental methods used	*I can add, subtract, multiply and divide whole numbers and decimals in my head.*
⑥ **What's wrong?** ⑦ **Ink blots**				
Use efficient written methods to add or subtract integers and decimals, to multiply or divide integers or decimals by a one-digit integer, and to multiply two-digit or three-digit integers by a two-digit integer	● understand and use an appropriate non-calculator method for solving problems that involve multiplying and dividing any three-digit number by any two-digit number	● use efficient written methods of addition and subtraction and of short multiplication and division ● multiply a simple decimal by a single digit	● knows when it is necessary to use efficient written methods ● can add or subtract integers and decimals using efficient written methods ● can multiply or divide integers and decimals using efficient written methods	*I can add, subtract, multiply and divide whole numbers and decimals using efficient written methods.*
⑧ **Which key?**				
Use a calculator to solve problems involving multi-step calculations	● use a calculator where appropriate to calculate fractions/percentages of quantities/measurements, e.g. ● find fractions of quantities such as 3/8 of 980 ● find percentages such as 15% of 360g	● use inverse operations, e.g. ● use a calculator and inverse operations to find missing numbers, including decimals ● solve problems with or without a calculator	● knows when to use a calculator to work out a calculation ● can choose specific function keys to carry out a calculation ● can explain the strategy used to find a solution	*I can use a calculator to solve problems involving more than one step.*
⑨ **Best estimates**				
Use approximations, inverse operations and tests of divisibility to estimate and check results	● approximate to check answers to problems are of the correct magnitude ● check solutions by applying inverse operations or estimating using approximations ● check results, considering whether these are reasonable	● check reasonableness of results with reference to the context or size of numbers ● develop own strategies for solving problems	● knows the importance of estimating the answer to a calculation before starting ● can work mentally when finding approximate answers to calculations	*I can estimate and check the result of a calculation.*

BLOCK A

Activities

Prior learning
Children can use an appropriate strategy to find missing numbers given certain clues and they can explain the method they used to find the solution.

Framework objective
Explain reasoning and conclusions, using words, symbols or diagrams as appropriate

Vocabulary
problem, solution, method, strategy, jotting, explain, reason, predict, relationship

Resources
Worksheet: What am I?

① What am I?

Provide each child with a copy of the worksheet 'What am I?'. The children are asked to find missing numbers, given a range of clues. They are also required to explain how they obtained their solutions.

Teacher support
Less confident learners: Encourage these children to write out the puzzle as a number sentence using '?' to indicate the missing number. Provide them with puzzles containing single-digit or small two-digit numbers to start with.
More confident learners: Encourage these children to work with more complicated number puzzles, sometimes including fractions or decimal numbers.

Common misconceptions
Children cannot explain clearly how they obtained a solution or, if they had difficulty, where the problems occurred.
Encourage the children to make written jottings or number sentences to go with their explanations and to bring each step of the puzzle to a conclusion before moving on.

Probing questions
● If you start with the answer and work backwards to the missing number, what operations have to be used this time?
● How can you check the problem at the end to see if the correct solution has been reached?

Next steps
Support: Make sure children are confident about writing down this type of problem and that each stage of finding the solution follows on logically from another. Refer back to Year 6 Block A Unit 1.
Extension: Extend to examine more general number statements with children. For example: *The numbers 27, 32 and 44 can never be multiples of 5. Is this statement true or false? Explain how you know.* Refer also to Year 6 Block E Unit 1.

Activity ②

Prior learning
Children can solve multi-step problems and choose the correct calculation strategies at each stage of the process.

Framework objective
Solve multi-step problems and problems involving fractions, decimals and percentages; choose and use appropriate calculation strategies at each stage, including calculator use

Vocabulary
problem, solution, calculate, calculation, calculator, operation, answer, method, strategy, jotting, explain, reason, add, subtract, multiply, divide, sum, total, difference, product, quotient, greater than, less than, increase, decrease, reduce

Resources
Resource sheets: Your choice, Flashcards, Self-assessment

② Your choice

This is a practical task to ensure that the children can identify the operations they would use in multi-step problems and what methods they would employ to find the solution. Cut out the problems from the 'Your choice' resource sheet as well as the flashcards (one set per pair). The children should work in pairs. One child should read out two of the problems while the other uses flashcards, first to show what operations are needed and then to indicate the method they would employ to find the answer. The pair should then work together on finding the answer. They should swap roles for the other two problems. [Answers: **1.** 139 children, £1727.50; **2.** 30% of 90 (27); **3.** John, 38cm, John 9cm, Sanjay 53cm, Beth 47cm; **4.** Six times, £270.] Decide whether to use the self-assessment sheet for the children to record their achievements and what they need to do next.

Teacher support
Less confident learners: Make sure these children write down all their working out so that operations and methods can be analysed fully.
More confident learners: Invite these children to make up their own multi-step problems using everyday situations they encounter at school or at home.

Common misconceptions
Children misinterpret key words and confuse operations when they are trying to solve the problem.
Spend time revising and discussing the meaning of key words and the operations they imply – for example, increase (add), find the difference (subtract), product (multiply) and quotient (divide).

Probing questions
● What clues do you look for when deciding what operations need to be carried out?
● How do you decide which operation should be done first?

Next steps
Support: Look closely at the type and detail of the operations children used and the methods they employed. Refer back to Year 6 Block A Unit 1.
Extension: Discuss with children what alternative approaches might have been used to calculate answers. Ask: *Would working out estimated answers first have proved useful?* Refer also to Year 6 Block C Unit 1.

Activity

Prior learning
Children can use decimals with up to three places and order them on a number line. They can round decimals to the nearest whole number or the nearest tenth.

Framework objective
Use decimal notation for tenths, hundredths and thousandths; partition, round and order decimals with up to three places and position them on the number line

Vocabulary
place value, digit, numeral, partition, integer, decimal point, decimal place, tenths, hundredths, thousandths, round, order, number line

Resources
Interactive activity: Bricks
Resource sheet: Empty number lines (for support)
Classroom resources: individual whiteboards and pens

③ Building bricks

In this interactive task, children are asked to identify and order three-place decimals. Five bricks, each showing a number between 0 and 10 with three decimal places, have to be placed in the correct order in the wall, lowest at the bottom.

Teacher support
Less confident learners: Provide these children with an 'Empty number lines' resource sheet, together with individual whiteboards and pens, to try out their solutions first. Alternatively, fix the highest and lowest numbers in place and ask children to order the remaining ones.
More confident learners: Ask these children to calculate what would need to be added to the decimal numbers on each brick to make 10.

Common misconceptions
Children remain confused about the value of decimal numbers.
Reinforce place value by displaying large charts showing column values, such as:
U . t h th

Probing questions
● What happens when ordering decimal numbers if the same digit occurs in the same place (for example, 6.52 and 6.57 or 8.203 and 8.205)?
● Which numbers are the hardest to put in order? Why?

Next steps
Support: Use digit cards and a decimal point card to reinforce place value in decimal numbers. For example: *What is the largest number with one decimal place you can make from 3, 6, 9?* (96.3) Refer back to Year 6 Block A Unit 1.
Extension: Work on questions where decimal numbers are added to the digits already in decimal numbers. For example, $6.3 + 1/10$, $7.52 + 3/100$ and $4.192 + 6/1000$.

Activity ④

Prior learning
Children can know and use multiplication facts up to 10 × 10 and relate these facts to decimal numbers.

Framework objective
Use knowledge of place value and multiplication facts to 10 × 10 to derive related multiplication and division facts involving decimals (e.g. 0.8 × 7, 4.8 ÷ 6)

Vocabulary
place value, digit, numeral, decimal point, decimal place, multiply, multiplication, divide, division

Resources
Interactive activity: Partner time

④ Partner time

In the interactivity activity 'Partner time' the children carry out a matching task in which two lists of numbers are given in vertical lists. They need to drag the arrows to match up each decimal multiplication or division problem with the correct answer.

Teacher support
Less confident learners: Play multiplication and division number games frequently so that children's knowledge of their times tables is very sound.
More confident learners: Encourage these children to work more with decimal points in both the numbers they are multiplying or dividing (for example, 8 × 4 = 32 so 0.8 × 0.4 = ? and 36 ÷ 9 = 4 so 3.6 ÷ 0.9 = ?).

Common misconceptions
Children do not realise that the position of the decimal point in numbers being multiplied will affect the position of the decimal point in the answer. For example, 0.7 (one place) × 0.3 (one place) = 0.21 (two places).
Ensure answers are checked using a calculator so decimal points have been positioned in the correct place.

Probing questions
● How many different multiplication and division facts using decimal numbers can be derived from a number such as 48?
● What if you started instead with 4.8 or 9.6?

Next steps
Support: Revise derived numbers with children so they fully understand the value of each digit in a decimal number (for example, 0.36 = 36/100 or 3/10 and 6/100). Refer back to Year 6 Block A Unit 1.
Extension: Work on number patterns associated with derived numbers, such as 3.5 × 2 = 7, 3.5 × 3 = 10.5, 3.5 × 4 = 14, 3.5 × 5 = 17.5. Refer also to Year 6 Block B Unit 1 and Block E Unit 1.

Activity ⑤

Prior learning
Children can add, subtract, multiply and divide simple decimal numbers mentally with confidence. They can use decimal notation with units and tenths.

Framework objective
Calculate mentally with integers and decimals: U.t ± U.t, TU × U, TU ÷ U, U.t × U, U.t ÷ U

Vocabulary
problem, solution, calculate, calculation, operation, answer, method, strategy, place value, numeral, digit, integer, decimal point, decimal place, add, subtract, multiply, divide

Resources
Resource sheets: Beat the clock, Self-assessment
Classroom resources: stopwatch/timer

⑤ Beat the clock

Display the resource sheet 'Beat the clock' on the whiteboard. Working in pairs, ask the children to work through the 20 questions as quickly as they can. The questions can be read from the board or read aloud by their partner. One child does the first ten questions; the other child does the second ten questions. They should check each others' answers and record the time on a stopwatch or timer. Invite them to try the same activity several days later to see if they can improve on their times. Decide whether to use the self-assessment sheet for the children to record their achievements and what they need to do next.

Teacher support
Less confident learners: Set these children realistic time targets so that initially they have the opportunity to complete the questions successfully.
More confident learners: Devise mental speed check activities for these children that involve mental calculations involving simple amounts of money.

Common misconceptions
Children believe there is only one set method to find solutions for each of the four operations.
Show the children how each solution can be found in a number of different ways. Stress how they must choose the method they find most comfortable to work with mentally.

Probing questions
● Which of the four operations did you find easiest to work with mentally? Explain why.
● When you have reached a solution, can you say the value of each digit in the decimal answer?

Next steps
Support: Ask children to place their answers on a place value chart or board and to say answers aloud. For example, 4.3 is 4 and $3/10$ and 5.25 is 5 and $25/100$ or 5 and $2/10$ and $5/100$. Refer back to Year 6 Block A Unit 1.
Extension: Encourage children to work on examples of inverse operations of decimal numbers to check their answers. For example, if 6.2 + 4.3 = 10.5, then 10.5 − 4.3 = 6.2 and if 4.5 × 4 = 18 then 18 ÷ 4 = 4.5 (and so on). Refer also to Year 6 Block D Units 1, 2 and 3.

Unit 2  Counting, partitioning and calculating

Activities ⑥ and ⑦

Prior learning
Children can use reliable written methods to add or subtract integers and decimal numbers. They can also use reliable written methods to multiply or divide simple decimals and larger whole numbers.

Framework objective
Use efficient written methods to add and subtract integers and decimals, to multiply and divide integers or decimals by a one-digit integer, and to multiply two-digit and three-digit integers by a two-digit integer

Vocabulary
calculate, calculation, operation, answer, method, strategy, jotting, explain, place value, digit, number, integer, decimal point, decimal place

Resources
Display page: Ink blots
Worksheets: What's wrong?, Ink blots
Resource sheet: Multiplication square (for support)

⑥ What's wrong?

On the worksheet 'What's wrong?' children are given a series of calculations involving addition and subtraction (some questions involve decimal numbers). They have to work through the questions and find the deliberate mistakes.

Teacher support
Less confident learners: Make sure these children are confident about switching from horizontal to vertical written methods of addition/subtraction.
More confident learners: Encourage children to check answers by using the inverse method, i.e. checking additions by subtracting and checking subtractions by adding.

Common misconceptions
Children do not line up digits correctly, especially when they are adding or subtracting decimal numbers.
Write digits under place value column labels if necessary, and ensure decimal points are always lined up underneath each other.

Probing questions
● In which order should the columns be added?
● When subtracting, should the top row be taken from the bottom row or vice versa?

Next steps
Support: Continue to revise setting calculations down in columns.
Extension: Challenge this group to devise some addition or subtraction calculations in which random missing numbers have to be found. Refer also to Year 6 Block D Units 1, 2 and 3.

⑦ Ink blots

Reveal the display page 'Ink blots' and go through the questions with the children. Then hand out the corresponding worksheet and ask the children to complete it individually.

Teacher support
Less confident learners: Provide multiplication squares as additional support.
More confident learners: Encourage these children to try out more than one method for both multiplying and dividing decimal numbers.

Common misconceptions
Digits are carried to the wrong columns when multiplying, and decimal points are located in the wrong place at the end of calculations.
Carry out careful approximation activities first so children have a closer idea of what the answer should really be.

Probing questions
● When is it advisable to use full written methods for calculations as opposed to working mentally or using jottings?

Next steps
Support: Ask children to investigate the best way of checking to see if their calculations are correct. Refer back to Year 6 Block A Unit 1.
Extension: Ask children to create word problems to demonstrate the calculation skills used in these last two activities. Refer also to Year 6 Block D Units 1, 2 and 3.

Activity ⑧

Prior learning
Children can use a calculator to solve problems involving more than one step. They can also use an alternative method to check that their solution is correct.

Framework objective
Use a calculator to solve problems involving multi-step calculations

Vocabulary
problem, solution, calculate, calculation, calculator, operation, answer, method, strategy, explain, reason, display, enter, clear, function key, number sentence

Resources
Worksheet: Which key?
Classroom resources: calculators

⑧ Which key?

This is a practical assessment to be carried out in pairs or with the teacher/ teaching assistant working with a small group. Hand out copies of the worksheet 'Which key?'. For each of the number sentences shown on the worksheet, ask the children to write the correct function into the blank 'keys'. When they have completed the sheet, ask them to use calculators to check their answers.

Teacher support
Less confident learners: Make sure that these children are familiar with the four main function keys (add, subtract, multiply and divide) on the calculator keypad.
More confident learners: Ask these children to write the strategy they used to find the answer and then explain it to one of their classmates.

Common misconceptions
Children believe the calculator is at fault when they have entered the information incorrectly.
Point out that a calculator will not give the correct answer unless the information is entered in a way the calculator can 'read'.

Probing questions
● In which order did you enter the information into the calculator?
● What strategy did you use to check that your answer was correct?

BLOCK A

Support: Did children look for clues about which function keys to try or did they use a trial and improvement method until they obtained the correct solution? Refer back to Year 6 Block A Unit 1.

Extension: Challenge children to devise their own problems using the four function keys on the calculator. Refer also to Year 6 Block B Units 2 and 3, Block C Units 2 and 3, Block D Units 1, 2 and 3, and Block E Units 1, 2 and 3.

Activity ⑨

Prior learning
Children can round integers to the nearest 10, 100 and 1000 and round decimal numbers to the nearest whole number.

Framework objective
Use approximations, inverse operations and tests of divisibility to estimate and check results

Vocabulary
digit, numeral, integer, decimal point, decimal place, round, estimate, approximate, approximately, add, subtract, multiply, divide

Resources
Resource sheets: Best estimates, Self-assessment
Classroom resources: calculators, individual whiteboards and pens

⑨ Best estimates

This is an oral activity for individual children or small groups of two or three. Call out the questions on the 'Best estimates' resource sheet to the children along with the three alternative estimates. Ask the children to write their best estimates on their individual whiteboards. Once they have completed this, provide them with calculators so they can work out exact answers and compare results. Decide whether to use the self-assessment sheet for the children to record achievements and what they need to do next.

Teacher support
Less confident learners: Help these children with rounding so that they have tidy numbers to work with when estimating answers.
More confident learners: Ask children to predict whether their estimates will be greater or less than the exact answer when calculated, and to explain why.

Common misconceptions
Children tend to overestimate and go for numbers that are far higher than the exact answer.
Emphasise that estimates that are lower than the exact answer can, in fact, be closer to it than those that go over.

Probing questions
● What strategy did you use to arrive at your estimated answer?
● Did you find it easier to work with integers or decimal numbers? Why?

Next steps
Support: Go back over the questions and stress the clues and evidence that pointed towards one answer rather than the others. Refer back to Year 6 Block A Unit 1.
Extension: Set children an open-ended problem where they can extend their estimation skills. For example: *How many minutes do you spend in school during a school year?* Refer also to Year 6 Block D Unit 1.

Unit 3 ◾ Counting, partitioning and calculating

Introduction

The lessons in this unit provide children with more practice in using decimal numbers as well as adding and subtracting numbers mentally. Using and applying mathematics activities feature again and children work on word problems involving money, mass and capacity, and percentages. Formal written calculation methods are examined again, this time including multiplication. Children also estimate answers and check results using approximation.

Framework objectives	Assessment focuses		Success criteria for Year 6	Learning outcomes
	Level 5	**Level 4**		
① Counting sticks				
Explain reasoning and conclusions, using words, symbols or diagrams as appropriate	● draw simple conclusions of their own and give an explanation of their reasoning, e.g. ● explain and justify their methods and solution ● identify more complex patterns, making generalisations in words and begin to express generalisations using symbolic notation	● search for a solution by trying out ideas of their own, e.g. ● check their methods and justify answers ● identify patterns as they work and form their own generalisations/rules in words	● can look at a sequence and predict how it will continue ● can adopt a systematic approach when solving sequence problems ● can use symbols/ diagrams in sequence problems	*I can explain my reasoning and conclusions, using symbols to represent unknown numbers.*
② You choose				
Solve multi-step problems, and problems involving fractions, decimals and percentages; choose and use appropriate calculation strategies at each stage, including calculator use	● identify and obtain necessary information to carry through a task and solve mathematical problems, e.g. ● recognise information that is important to solving the problem, determine what is missing and develop lines of enquiry ● break a several-step problem or investigation into simpler steps	● develop own strategies for solving problems, e.g. ● make their own suggestions of ways to tackle a range of problems ● make connections to previous work ● pose and answer questions related to a problem ● check answers and ensure solutions make sense in the context of the problem	● uses an appropriate strategy when solving problems ● makes up suitable problems when presented with an outcome ● can identify and define key vocabulary in problems ● can explain the method used to find a solution	*I can solve problems involving more than one step. I can explain the reason for my choice of method and say whether I think it was effective.*
③ Dice roll				
Use decimal notation for tenths, hundredths and thousandths; partition, round and order decimals with up to three places, and position them on the number line	● use equivalence between fractions, e.g. ● convert fractions such as 2/5 into tenths or hundredths and express them as decimals or percentages and vice versa ● round decimals to the nearest decimal place ● order fractions and decimals, e.g. ● order decimals that have a mixture of one, two or three decimal places	● recognise approximate proportions of a whole and use simple fractions and percentages to describe these, e.g. ● recognise simple equivalence between fractions, decimals and percentages, e.g. 1/2, 1/4, 1/10, 3/4 ● order decimals to three decimal places	● knows the place value of numbers to three decimal places ● can order sets of decimal numbers	*I can use decimals with up to three places and order them on a number line. I can partition decimals with three places.*

Unit 3 📖 Counting, partitioning and calculating

Framework objectives	Assessment focuses		Success criteria for Year 6	Learning outcomes
	Level 5	Level 4		
④ Find me				
Calculate mentally with integers and decimals: U.t ± U.t, TU × U, TU ÷ U, U.t × U, U.t ÷ U	● use all four operations with decimals to two places, e.g. ● add and subtract numbers that do not have the same number of decimal places ● multiply or divide decimal numbers by a single digit, e.g. 31.62 × 7	● use a range of mental methods of computation with all operations, e.g. ● calculate complements to 1000 ● recall multiplication facts up to 10 × 10 and quickly derive corresponding division facts, e.g. ● use their knowledge of tables and place value in calculations with multiples of 10 such as 30 × 7, 180 ÷ 3	● uses knowledge of tables and place value to multiply or divide whole numbers and decimals mentally ● can make up mental calculation questions when provided with an answer ● knows what will happen when a decimal number is multiplied by 10 or 100	*I can add, subtract, multiply and divide whole numbers and decimals in my head.*
⑤ Target number				
Use efficient written methods to add and subtract integers and decimals, to multiply and divide integers and decimals by a one-digit integer, and to multiply two-digit and three-digit integers by a two-digit integer	● understand and use an appropriate non-calculator method for solving problems that involve multiplying or dividing any three-digit number by any two-digit number	● use efficient written methods of addition and subtraction, and of short multiplication and division e.g. ● calculate 1202 + 45 + 367 or 1025 − 336 ● add and subtract decimals to two places ● multiply a simple decimal by a single digit, e.g. ● calculate 36.2 × 8	● knows when it is necessary to use efficient written methods ● can use known number facts to find a target number ● can use all four operations ● can decide which strategies are the best ones to use	*I can use efficient written methods to add, subtract, multiply and divide integers and decimal numbers. I can calculate the answer to HTU ÷ U and U.t ÷ U to one or two decimal places.*
⑥ Home decorating				
Use a calculator to solve problems involving multi-step calculations	● use a calculator where appropriate to calculate fractions/percentages of quantities/measurements, e.g. ● find fractions of quantities such as 3/8 of 980 ● find percentages such as 15% of 360g	● use inverse operations, e.g. ● use a calculator and inverse operations to find missing numbers, including decimals ● solve problems with or without a calculator	● knows when a calculator is needed for solving a problem ● can work with the calculator, orally explaining each step used to solve a problem ● can check answers on the calculator using a different method	*I can use a calculator to solve problems with more than one step.*
⑦ Shopping: approximations				
Use approximations, inverse operations and tests of divisibility to estimate and check results	● approximate to check answers to problems are of the correct magnitude ● check solutions by applying inverse operations or estimating using approximations ● check results, considering whether these are reasonable, e.g. ● check as they work, spotting and correcting errors and reviewing methods	● check the reasonableness of results with reference to the context or size of numbers ● develop their own strategies for solving problems, e.g. ● check answers and ensure solutions make sense in the context of the problem ● review their work and approaches	● rounds off integers to the nearest 10, 100 or 1000 ● rounds off money amounts to the nearest 10p ● can check answers obtained	*I can estimate and check the result of a calculation.*

Activity ①

Prior learning
Children can spot the pattern made in a sequence of shapes and predict how the sequence will continue. They can explain the method they used to find the solution.

Framework objective
Explain reasoning and conclusions, using words, symbols or diagrams as appropriate

Vocabulary
problem, solution, equation, operation, answer, method, strategy, explain, reason, rule, formula, term, represent

Resources
Worksheet: Counting sticks
Classroom resources: coloured sticks (for support); squared, isometric or dotty paper (for extension)

① Counting sticks

Provide the children with copies of the worksheet 'Counting sticks'. They are asked to look at the sequence of shapes provided and work out how many sticks will be needed to make eight shapes in each sequence.

Teacher support
Less confident learners: These children may need to be provided with supplies of coloured sticks so that they can actually make some of the early shapes in the sequence.
More confident learners: Provide these children with only the first two items in the sequence or ask them to predict the pattern further ahead (say, in tenth or in twelfth position).

Common misconceptions
Children forget that some sticks will occur in two of the shapes and therefore count them twice.
Encourage the children to adopt a systematic approach when counting sticks so that some of them do not get counted twice – for example, top row first, then centre row, then bottom row.

Probing questions
● Is the problem easier to solve if actual sticks are provided to make the patterns in the sequence?
● Are sequence activities involving shapes easier or more difficult to solve than those involving only numbers?

Next steps
Support: Provide opportunities to continue with the tactile experience of making sequence patterns with sticks if this helps in finding the solution. Refer back to Year 6 Block A Units 1 and 2.
Extension: Provide squared, isometric or dotty paper so that children can devise and draw their own sequences using shapes such as squares, rectangles and triangles. Refer also to Year 6 Block E Units 1 and 2.

Activity ②

Prior learning
Children can solve problems involving more than one step, and can explain the reason for their choice of method and say whether they think it was effective.

Framework objective
Solve multi-step problems and problems involving fractions, decimals and percentages; choose and use appropriate calculation strategies at each stage, including calculator use

Vocabulary
problem, solution, calculate, calculation, calculator, operation, answer, method, strategy, jotting, explain, add, subtract, multiply, divide, sum, total, difference, product, quotient, greater than, less than, increase, decrease, reduce

Resources
Worksheet: You choose
Classroom resources: calculators

② You choose

Provide each child with a copy of the worksheet 'You choose'. The children are presented with the numbers used in a calculation and have to make up their own word problems to fit the numbers.

Teacher support
Less confident learners: Revise the meaning of key words in the vocabulary list (total, difference, product and so on) so that children have a good variety of suitable words at their disposal.
More confident learners: Challenge these children to come up with several word problems for each number statement and/or to demonstrate how they used a different method to obtain the same answer.

Common misconceptions
Children think there is only one fixed method for finding the answer.
Show the children there are other possibilities. They should not be forced to adopt one procedure but should utilise the calculation method they feel most comfortable with.

Probing questions
● What are the key features to look out for when solving a word problem?
● What clues do you look for in the wording of the question?

Next steps
Support: Ask children to talk through the problems they have devised and explain in detail how they fit the number statements provided. Refer back to Year 6 Block A Unit 2.
Extension: Challenge children to devise word problems from their own number statements containing at least three different operations and/or the use of brackets. Refer also to Year 6 Block D Unit 2 and Block E Units 1 and 3.

Activity ③

Prior learning
Children can use decimals with up to three decimal places and order them on a number line. They can partition decimals with three decimal places.

Framework objective
Use decimal notation for tenths, hundredths and thousandths; partition, round and order decimals with up to three places and position them on the number line

Vocabulary
place value, digit, numeral, partition, integer, decimal point, decimal place, tenths, hundredths, thousandths, round, order

Resources
Resource sheet: Self-assessment
Classroom resources: calculators, strips of large-squared paper, 1–6 dice

③ Dice roll

This is a game for two players with two dice and a calculator. Each player has a strip of ten squares. Zero is written in the left-hand square, with 6 in the square at the right-hand end. The players take it in turns to roll the dice to generate two numbers. Each player then decides the order in which to divide the two numbers. For example, 3 and 4 can give $3 \div 4 = 0.75$ or $4 \div 3 = 1.333$ (recurring). The result of the division is entered in a space on the grid. All numbers on the grid must be in order of size. The same number cannot be entered twice. The first player to complete their grid wins. In case of stalemate, the player with most numbers entered wins. Decide whether to use the self-assessment sheet for the children to record their achievements and what they need to do next.

Teacher support
Less confident learners: Ensure that the correct information is entered into the calculator and that the correct decimal number is read from the display at the end of the calculation.
More confident learners: Encourage these children to carry out some of the division tasks involved without using the calculator.

Common misconceptions
Children think that the more numbers there are after the decimal point the smaller the number is (for example, that 1.66666 is smaller than 1.5).
Continue to emphasise that with decimal numbers it is the position in which a digit occurs that gives it its value, not the size of the digit or the number of digits there are.

Probing questions
● Can you tell me a number with two decimal places that rounds to 5.0 when rounded to the nearest tenth?
● Explain to others what happens to a decimal fraction when multiplied by 10 or 100.

Next steps
Support: Make sure that children are including the decimal point when recording a decimal fraction and do not realise they have written a whole number. Refer back to Year 6 Block A Units 1 and 2.
Extension: Challenge children to devise their own game using simple equipment to test their knowledge of sorting decimal numbers and placing them on a number line. Refer also to Year 6 Block E Unit 3.

Activity ④

Prior learning
Children can add, subtract, multiply and divide whole numbers and decimals in their head.

Framework objective
Calculate mentally with integers and decimals: U.t ± U.t, TU × U, TU ÷ U, U.t × U, U.t ÷ U

Vocabulary
problem, solution, calculate, calculation, operation, answer, strategy, method, place value, number, digit, integer, decimal point, decimal place, add, subtract, multiply, divide

Resources
Interactive activity: Find me

④ Find me

Reveal the interactive activity 'Find me'. The children are required to work out the calculations and then use the pop-up keypad to type the answers into the boxes provided.

Teacher support
Less confident learners: Remind these children to think carefully about the positioning of the decimal point in the answer.
More confident learners: Encourage these children to devise some questions in which there are three items in the number statement (for example, 6.3 + 4.9 + 1.5 and 27 × 4 × 2).

Common misconceptions
Some children think the point is the decimal fraction, lacking understanding of place value.
These children require more experience of explaining the value of each of the digits for numbers that involve decimal notation.

Probing questions
● What simple method can you use to check that your answer is correct?
● Which did you find easier to calculate mentally, multiplying or dividing decimal numbers? Explain why.

Next steps
Support: Re-emphasise to children that in decimal numbers the decimal point is a marker than separates whole numbers from fractions. Refer back to Year 6 Block A Units 1 and 2.
Extension: Ask children to think of practical situations where it is important to be able to carry out quick mental calculations especially involving decimal numbers. (For example, when shopping.) Ask questions such as: *What is the total of £1.25 and £2.50?* Refer also to Year 6 Block D Units 1, 2 and 3.

BLOCK A

Activity ⑤

Prior learning
Children can use reliable written methods to multiply two-digit or three-digit integers by a two-digit integer. They can describe and explain the method they have used for their calculations.

Framework objective
Use efficient written methods to add and subtract integers and decimals, to multiply and divide integers or decimals by a one-digit integer, and to multiply two-digit and three-digit integers by a two-digit integer

Vocabulary
calculate, calculation, operation, answer, method, strategy, jotting, explain, number, digit, integer, multiply, multiplication, product

Resources
Interactive activity: Target number
Resource sheets: Target number, Self-assessment

⑤ Target number

Show the class the interactive activity 'Target number'. In this activity the children are encouraged to use known number facts in order to find the target number. Players click 'go' to generate five number cards. A target number will automatically appear on the screen. Tell the children to try to match (or nearly match) the target number by writing number sentences that use the numbers on the cards and some (or all) of the four operations (+, -, ÷, ×).

Teacher support
Less confident learners: Support these children by providing them with the resource sheet 'Target number'. Decide whether to use the self-assessment sheet for these children to record their achievements and what they need to do next.
More confident learners: Encourage these children to use square numbers. Ask questions such as: *Can you reach the target number more quickly using this method?*

Common misconceptions
Children cannot explain the numbers they choose when trying to make the target number.
As the process is important, invite individual children to write their calculation on the on-screen notepad, demonstrating that it matches (or nearly matches) the target.

Probing questions
● What strategies are the most efficient? How do these strategies help you to 'hit the target'?
● What tips would you give somebody who was new to this activity?

Next steps
Support: Remind children that multiplication is a shortcut method of carrying out addition where the sets have the same number of members. Remind them also that the order in which numbers are multiplied does not affect the answer. Refer back to Year 6 Block A Unit 2.
Extension: Encourage children to demonstrate that they are conversant with at least two efficient written methods for multiplying two-digit or three-digit integers by a two-digit integer. Refer also to Year 6 Block D Units 1, 2 and 3.

BLOCK A

Activity ⑥

Prior learning
Children can use a calculator to solve problems with more than one step.

Framework objective
Use a calculator to solve problems involving multi-step calculations

Vocabulary
problem, solution, calculate, calculation, calculator, operation, answer, method, strategy, explain, reason, display, enter, clear, function key, number sentence

Resources
Display page: Home decorating
Worksheet: Home decorating
Classroom resources: calculators

⑥ Home decorating

This is a practical oral activity that can be carried out in pairs or with the teacher/teaching assistant working with a small group of children. Reveal the display page 'Home decorating' and go through the problems with the children. Then hand out the corresponding worksheet for the children to complete individually. They need to be able to explain what they are doing during each step of the process.

Teacher support
Less confident learners: Remind these children that it is easy to make errors when keying in information and that it is important to check their answers.
More confident learners: Encourage these children to try out various methods of checking their answers – for example, by using a different method or by using the inverse operation.

Common misconceptions
Children think that, as a matter of course, the calculator will store information as a series of different operations are carried out.
Show these children how the memory facility works and how this might be beneficial in working out some calculations.

Probing questions
● What do you need to enter into the calculator in order to carry out the calculation?
● Show me how to read amounts of money shown in the calculator display. (For example, £5.2 is actually £5.20.)

Next steps
Support: Remind children always to think carefully about which operation key to use and how to enter the calculation. Refer back to Year 6 Block A Units 1 and 2.
Extension: Challenge children to make up their own word problems using, specifically, metric measures and money amounts. Refer also to Year 6 Block B Units 2 and 3; Block C Units 2 and 3; Block D Units 2 and 3; Block E Units 2 and 3.

Activity ⑦

Prior learning
Children can round integers to the nearest 10, 100 or 1000. They can round off money amounts to the nearest 10p.

Framework objective
Use approximations, inverse operations and tests of divisibility to estimate and check results

Vocabulary
digit, numeral, integer, decimal point, decimal place, round, estimate, approximate, approximately

Resources
Interactive activity: Shopping: approximations
Classroom resources: individual whiteboards and pens

⑦ Shopping: approximations

Show the children the interactive activity 'Shopping: approximations'. This activity is designed to encourage children to round amounts prior to adding them to find totals and then to check their estimates against calculations. They should work out the answers to the questions on their individual whiteboards so that calculations can be discussed with others.

Teacher support
Less confident learners: Initially, ask these children to round amounts to the nearest £ to give them confidence.
More confident learners: Encourage these children to estimate the cost of all the goods in the shop.

Common misconceptions
Children think that the same approach should be used when working out the answers to all shopping calculations.
Point out to children that very simple calculations can be done mentally, some may require formal written methods and the more complicated ones may require a calculator.

Probing questions
● What would each item cost if it was rounded to the nearest pound?
● What would be the fewest number of notes and coins that could be used to pay the exact amount for each item?

Next steps
Support: Go through the children's individual calculations on their whiteboards to ensure that no errors have been made. Refer back to Year 6 Block A Units 1 and 2.
Extension: Ask children to show evidence in their calculations that they have checked the answers using the inverse operation (in this case, subtraction). Refer also to Year 6 Block D Units 2 and 3.

Units 1, 2 & 3 🔲 Periodic assessment

These activities can be used at any time during the teaching of this block to assess those children that you think have achieved the objective. A grid highlighting the related assessment focuses and expected learning outcomes for each activity can be found on the CD-ROM.

Solving problems

Framework objective
Solve multi-step problems and problems involving fractions, decimals and percentages; choose and use appropriate calculation strategies at each stage, including calculator use

Learning outcomes
- I can solve problems involving more than one step.
- I can explain the reason for my choice of method and say whether I think it was effective.

Provide the children with the worksheet 'Solving problems'. This shows three word problems that have important pieces of information missing. When the children have decided what the information missing is, they are required to make up numbers for this part of the question and solve the problem.

Deriving decimal numbers

Framework objective
Use knowledge of place value and multiplication facts to 10 × 10 to derive related multiplication and division facts involving decimals

Learning outcome
- I can use table facts to work out other facts with decimals.

Provide the children with the worksheet 'Deriving decimal numbers'. They are required to find the missing decimal numbers in each of the statements on the sheet.

Written methods

Framework objective
Use efficient written methods to add and subtract integers and decimals, to multiply and divide integers and decimals by a one-digit integer, and to multiply two-digit and three-digit integers by a two-digit integer

Learning outcome
- I can multiply and divide whole numbers and decimals using efficient written methods.

Provide the children with the worksheet 'Written methods (1)'. They are asked to work out the solutions to the two calculations shown on the sheet, without a calculator, using two distinctly different written methods.
  Ask the children to show all their workings out and then talk through the stages of what they have done.

Name   Date

Solving problems

What information do you need to solve these problems?

1. Maths lessons take place in each day in school. How long is spent in maths lessons altogether during a normal school week?

Rewrite the problem including the missing information, then solve it:

_____

_____

Answer: _____

2. A farmer divides 345 sheep into equal numbers in order to put them into pens. How many sheep are there in each pen?

Rewrite the problem including the missing information, then solve it:

_____

_____

Answer: _____

3. Fencing panels measure 1.60m in length and cost £19.99 each. How much will it cost to complete the fence along one side of the garden?

Rewrite the problem including the missing information, then solve it:

_____

_____

Answer: _____

How easy?

Red
Amber
Green

How do you think you have done?

_____

_____

Name _____ Date _____

Deriving decimal numbers

Fill in the missing decimal numbers in these statements.

1. 0.8 × 0.3 = _____	**2.** 0.7 × _____ = 0.35
3. _____ × 0.3 = 0.27	**4.** 0.6 × 3 = _____
5. _____ × 7 = 5.6	**6.** 0.9 × _____ = 5.4
7. 8 × _____ = 6.4	**8.** 0.5 × 0.8 = _____
9. 5.2 × _____ = 52	**10.** _____ × 10 = 6.5

How easy?

Red
Amber
Green

How do you think you have done?

_____

_____

BLOCK B

Securing number facts, understanding shape

Expected prior learning

Check that children can already:
- propose a general statement involving numbers or shapes
- organise information in a table
- use knowledge of place value, addition and subtraction of two-digit numbers to derive sums, differences, doubles and halves of decimals (eg 6.5 ± 2.7, halve 5.6, double 0.34)
- identify pairs of factors of two-digit whole numbers and find common multiples
- recognise parallel and perpendicular lines
- identify, visualise and describe properties of rectangles, regular polygons and 3D solids.

Objectives overview

The text in this diagram identifies the focus of mathematics learning within the block.

Key aspects of learning
- Information processing
- Communication
- Reasoning
- Creative thinking

Patterns, relationships and properties of numbers and shapes; suggesting hypotheses

Mental methods: multiplication and division facts applied to decimals

Representing a problem using calculations, symbols, formulae, diagrams

BLOCK B: Securing number facts, understanding shape

Multiples, factors, primes and prime factors

Tables to 10 × 10; squares, squares of multiples of 10

Tests of divisibility

Visualising and classifying 3D and 2D shapes, including quadrilaterals

Making and drawing shapes

Using a calculator, including to find inverses

Unit 1 ⬜ Securing number facts, understanding shape

Introduction

The lessons in this block gives prominence to securing number facts in a range of contexts. Children investigate multiples, factors, primes and prime factors, and use the table facts to 10 × 10 to find squares of multiples of 10. They continue to explore patterns, relationships and properties of number. They consolidate mental methods of multiplying and dividing facts in the context of decimals. In addition, children describe and identify parallel and perpendicular edges and faces in classifying 2D and 3D shapes. They practise drawing shapes with accuracy, using knowledge of their properties.

Framework objectives	Assessment focuses		Success criteria for Year 6	Learning outcomes
	Level 5	Level 4		
① Sequences ② Express it!				
Represent and interpret sequences, patterns and relationships involving numbers and shapes; suggest and test hypotheses; construct and use simple expressions and formulae in words then symbols	● draw simple conclusions of their own and give an explanation of their reasoning, e.g. ● identify more complex patterns, making generalisations in words and begin to express generalisations using symbolic notation ● use examples and counter-examples to justify conclusions ● construct, express in symbolic form, and use simple formulae involving one or two operations	● search for a solution by trying out ideas of their own, e.g. ● identify patterns as they work and form their own generalisations/rules in words ● begin to use simple formulae expressed in words	● can describe the interval between terms and sequences ● can continue patterns that include decimals ● can construct sentences to describe expressions which can then be written as simple formulae ● can solve simple expressions such as 6y or $x - 4$	I can describe and explain sequences, patterns and relationships. I can suggest hypotheses and test them. I can write and use simple expressions in words and formulae.
③ Square number match				
Use knowledge of multiplication facts to derive quickly squares of numbers to 12 × 12 and the corresponding squares of multiples of 10	There is no assessment focus for this level	● recognise and describe number relationships including multiple, factor and square	● knows the meaning of the words multiple, factor and square number ● can work out the factors of two-digit numbers ● knows and recognises the square numbers up to 144 and from this can square multiples of 10	I can say the squares of numbers to 12 × 12 and work out the squares of multiples of 10.
④ Fact finder				
Use knowledge of place value and multiplication facts to 10 × 10 to derive related multiplication and division facts involving decimals	● use all four operations with decimals to two places, e.g. ● multiply or divide decimal numbers by a single digit, e.g. 31.62 × 7	● multiply a simple decimal by a single digit, e.g. ● calculate 36.2 × 8 ● quickly derive division facts that correspond to multiplication facts up to 10 × 10	● can work out calculations with multiples of 10 ● uses an efficient written method to multiply or divide a simple decimal by a single digit	I can use table facts to work out other facts with decimals.

■SCHOLASTIC

Unit 1 ◻ Securing number facts, understanding shape

Framework objectives	Assessment focuses		Success criteria for Year 6	Learning outcomes
	Level 5	Level 4		
⑤ Prime time				
Recognise that prime numbers have only two factors and identify prime numbers less than 100; find the prime factors of two-digit numbers	• recognise and use number patterns and relationships, e.g. ○ find two-digit prime numbers	• recognise and describe number relationships including multiple, factor and square	• can find prime numbers to 100 • explains a way of checking to see if a number is prime • is able to express any two-digit number as its prime factors	*I can work out which numbers less than 100 are prime numbers.*
⑥ Check your bill				

Use approximation, inverse operations and tests of divisibility to estimate and check results	• approximate to check answers to problems are of the correct magnitude
	• check solutions by applying inverse operations or estimating using approximations
	• check results, considering whether these are reasonable
		• check the reasonableness of results with reference to the context or size of numbers
		• develop own strategies for solving problems, e.g.
		  ○ check answers and ensure solutions make sense in the context of the problem
		  ○ review their work and approaches
			• approximates before solving a problem, then uses it to check the answer
			• recognises the information that is important to solve a problem and indicates what is not relevant
			• checks answers as they work, correcting errors as necessary
				I can estimate and check the calculations that I do.

⑦ Properties of 2D shapes				

Describe, identify and visualise parallel and perpendicular edges or faces; use these properties to classify 2D shapes and 3D solids	• use a wider range of properties of 2D and 3D shapes, e.g.
	  ○ understand 'parallel' and begin to understand 'perpendicular' in relation to edges or faces
		• use the properties of 2D and 3D shapes, e.g.
		  ○ recognise and name most quadrilaterals, e.g. trapezium, parallelogram, rhombus
			• recognises the names of most quadrilaterals
			• recognises lines of symmetry in shapes
			• can visualise shapes and recognise them in different orientations
			• understands the terms parallel and perpendicular
				I can classify 2D shapes with perpendicular or parallel sides.

⑧ Properties of 3D solids ⑨ In the net				
Make and draw shapes with increasing accuracy and apply knowledge of their properties	• use a wider range of properties of 2D and 3D shapes • reason about shapes, positions and movements, e.g. ○ visualise a 3D shape from its net and match vertices that will be joined	• use the properties of 2D and 3D shapes • make 3D models by linking given faces or edges	• can make 3D models using equipment such as Polydron • understands the terms 'parallel' and 'perpendicular' and uses these terms to describe 2D and 3D shapes • understands the terms face, edge and vertex • can produce nets for simple 3D shapes such as cubes and pyramids • can visualise a 3D shape from its net and match vertices/edges that will be joined	*I can make and draw shapes accurately.*

BLOCK B

Activities ① and ②

Prior learning
Children can propose a general statement involving numbers or shapes.

Framework objective
Represent and interpret sequences, patterns and relationships involving numbers and shapes; suggest and test hypotheses; construct and use simple expressions and formulae in words then symbols

Vocabulary
sequence, generalise, reasoning, predict, rule, formula, relationship, term

Resources
Interactive activity: Sequences
Worksheets: What's the rule?, Express it!

① Sequences

Display the interactive activity 'Sequences' on the whiteboard. Explain to the children that they will need to work out the interval between each term in order to fill the blank spaces. Once they have done this, they need to select the correct rule from the options provided in the dropdown menu below.

Teacher support
Less confident learners: Before identifying the missing terms, discuss the pattern in the sequence and check that the children have worked out the intervals.
More confident learners: Ask what the next term would be beyond that displayed, or work out the terms that would come at the beginning of the sequences.

Common misconceptions
Children do not realise that incremental increase can be unequal.
Ensure that these children use jottings on the sequences to work out each increase.

Probing questions
● Do all number sequences increase?
● How can you work out a sequence given just the first two terms?
● How can you work out the first term in a sequence if given the second, third and fourth terms?

Next steps
Support: Ask children to complete just section 1 of the worksheet 'What's the rule?' Check that they understand that some sequences may increase in different steps (for example, +1, then +2, then +3, and so on). Refer back to Year 5 Block B Unit 3.
Extension: Ask these children to complete section 2 of the worksheet 'What's the rule?' Check that they understand that there could be two operations for each step (for example, double the number, then add 2). Refer also to Year 6 Block B Unit 2.

② Express it!

Provide each child with a copy of the worksheet 'Express it!'. Ask the children to construct expressions using symbols and solve others by substituting numbers into them.

Unit 1 Securing number facts, understanding shape

BLOCK B

Teacher support
Less confident learners: Make sure that children understand that if a number is placed next to a symbol, the missing operation is '×' ($2n$ stands for $2 \times n$).
More confident learners: Move these children on quickly to the expressions that involve fractions such as $\frac{e}{c}$. Encourage them, in pairs, to come up with expressions of their own.

Common misconceptions
Children forget the missing operation between the number and the symbol. They do not recognise that fractions need to be expressed by dividing the numerator by the denominator.
Encourage these children to make jottings to expand each expression so they can see the operations needed.

Probing questions
- Where in real life would you use symbols to take the place of numbers?
- How do you know that that expression is correct?

Next steps
Support: Provide further practice in expressing number sentences with symbols. Refer back to Year 5 Block B Unit 3.
Extension: Encourage children to create their own expressions for each other to solve (for example, 6 more than $y = 6 + y$). Refer also to Year 6 Block B Unit 2.

Activity ③

Prior learning
Children can instantly recall multiplication tables to 10 × 10 and know the square numbers up to 12 × 12.

Framework objective
Use knowledge of multiplication facts to derive quickly squares of numbers to 12 × 12 and the corresponding squares of multiples of 10

Vocabulary
square number, multiple, consecutive, product, power

Resources
Interactive activity: Square number match
Worksheet: All square
Classroom resources: individual whiteboards and pens

③ Square number match

Open the interactive activity 'Square number match'. Explain to the children that the answers in column 2 are the products of the calculations shown in column 1. Try some orally to put the activity into context (for example: *If 6 × 6 = 36, then what is 60 × 60? If 3^2 = 9, what is 900 × 900?*) Run the program, first asking the children to jot answers on their whiteboards. Next, choose individuals to come to the board and link the calculations with their products. Ask the rest of the class to check their own answers on their whiteboards. Finally, give out the worksheet 'All square' and ask the children to solve the problems using their understanding of square numbers.

Teacher support
Less confident learners: Encourage children to start with the answer to the single-digit square first, then moving to the corresponding multiple of 10.
More confident learners: Quickly move children on to the problems on the worksheet which involve two-step problems.

Common misconceptions

Children are confident in squaring single-digit numbers, but are uncertain as to the place value involved in multiples of 10.
Encourage children to check that the number of zeros in the answer matches the number of zeros in the calculation. For example 50 × 50 has two zeros, so there must be two zeros in the answer (2500).

Children forget that the squared sign (²) means multiply the number by itself, and instead multiply the number by 2.
Encourage children to jot down the whole calculation, so 5^2 expands to 5 × 5.

Probing questions

● What happens to the place value of the digits when multiplying in multiples of 10? ...100?
● What happens if you square a decimal number (for example 0.2)?

Next steps

Support: Ensure that these children are confident in squaring multiples of 10 in single-step problems before extending to multi-step ones. Refer back to Year 5 Block B Unit 3.
Extension: Introduce the cubed symbol ^{3}. Explain that it means the number is multiplied by itself three times. Explain the vocabulary 'power'. Provide some examples. *What would it mean if we write 4^5?* Refer to Year 6 Block B Unit 2.

Activity ④

Prior learning
Children can recall multiplication facts to 10 × 10. They can relate these facts to decimal numbers, for example 7 × 6 = 42, so 7 × 0.6 = 4.2.

Framework objective
Use knowledge of place value and multiplication facts to 10 × 10 to derive related multiplication and division facts involving decimals (e.g. 0.8 × 7, 4.8 ÷ 6)

Vocabulary
decimal, multiple, factor, place value, digit

Resources
Worksheet: Fact finder
Classroom resources: multiplication squares (for support)

---

④ Fact finder

Give out the worksheet 'Fact finder'. The children are asked to list factors of numbers and then derive the associated multiplication and division facts.

Teacher support
Less confident learners: Revise how to find factors of numbers and provide multiplication squares if needed.
More confident learners: Encourage these children to generate their own numbers to investigate.

Common misconceptions
Children are not able to find all the pairs of factors.
Encourage children to be systematic, starting with 1, then 2, and so on.

Some children may have difficulty in completing division facts, for example writing the calculation in the incorrect order (7 ÷ 4.2 = 0.6 instead of 4.2 ÷ 7).
Remind children that the number being divided must be written first.

▷ **Probing questions**
- What do you notice about the factors of 64 and 6.4? What has happened to the digits?
- How can your tables help you to work out the factors of decimals?

Next steps
Support: Provide further practice in deriving multiplication and division facts relating to decimals. Refer back to Year 5 Block B Unit 3.
Extension: Provide further practice in finding multiplication and division facts for decimals by generating calculations with missing number boxes (for example, 7.2 ÷ ▢ = 9). Refer also to Year 6 Block B Unit 2.

Activity ⑤

Prior learning
Children can identify pairs of factors of two-digit whole numbers.

Framework objective
Recognise that prime numbers have only two factors and identify prime numbers less than 100; find the prime factors of two-digit numbers

Vocabulary
factor, prime, prime factor, multiple

Resources
Worksheet: Prime time
Classroom resources: multiplication squares (for support)

⑤ Prime time

Give out copies of the worksheet 'Prime time'. The children are asked to find the factors of each of the given numbers and, from this, identify the prime numbers. They then move on to finding the prime factors of two-digit numbers.

Teacher support
Less confident learners: Make multiplication squares available and remind these children how to be systematic about finding the factors.
More confident learners: Quickly move these children on to the second part of the worksheet, finding prime factors.

Common misconceptions
Children fail to find all the factors of a number, so wrongly assume that a number is prime.
Show how to be systematic: divide by 2, then 3... rather than by random divisors.

Probing questions
- How can you make sure that all the factors of a number have been identified?
- How does finding all factors of a number help you to identify prime numbers?
- What is a more efficient way of writing the prime factors 2 × 2 × 2? (2^3)

Next steps
Support: Provide practice in working out prime factors of two-digit numbers. Refer back to Year 5 Block B Unit 3.
Extension: Use factors to multiply pairs of two-digit numbers (for example, 42 × 24 = 6 × 7 × 6 × 4 = 6^2 × 7 × 4 = 36 × 7 × 4 = 252 × 4 = 1008). Refer also to Year 6 Block B Unit 2.)

BLOCK B

Activity ⑥

Prior learning
Children can round integers to the nearest 10, 100 or 1000 and decimals to the nearest whole number.

Framework objective
Use approximations, tests of divisibility and inverse operations to estimate and check results

Vocabulary
integer, decimal, round, estimate, approximate, inverse, divisibility, operation

Resources
Display page: Check your bill
Resource sheet: Self-assessment

⑥ Check your bill

Reveal the display page 'Check your bill' and go through the questions with the children. Decide whether to use the self-assessment sheet for children to record their achievements and next steps.

Teacher support
Less confident learners: Ensure that these children have a sound knowledge of rounding in money contexts.
More confident learners: Encourage children to round to the nearest 50p for a more accurate approximation (for example, £10.37 = £10.50, rather than £10).

Common misconceptions
Children round incorrectly.
Provide number lines as an aid to rounding to the nearest 10 or 100.

Probing questions
- Why do we need to estimate?
- When do we use estimating in real-life situations?

Next steps
Support: Estimate in a range of situations (for example, rounding numbers on car number plates). Refer back to Year 5 Block B Unit 3.
Extension: Make it a requirement that children estimate answers whenever they perform calculations. Refer also to Year 6 Block B Unit 2.

Activity ⑦

Prior learning
Children can recognise parallel and perpendicular lines.

Framework objective
Describe, identify and visualise parallel and perpendicular edges or faces; use these properties to classify 2D shapes and 3D solids

Vocabulary
parallel, perpendicular, face, edge, vertex, vertices, regular, irregular, quadrilateral, adjacent

Resources
Display page: Properties of 2D shapes
Resource sheet: Self-assessment
Classroom resources: elastic bands, nail/peg boards (or dotty paper)

⑦ Properties of 2D shapes

Carry out this activity in small groups, with another adult. Ask children to make quadrilaterals on peg boards (or draw them on dotted paper) in response to given sets of criteria. Check that they understand the vocabulary and properties of their shapes. Go through the questions on the display pages 'Properties of 2D shapes'. Decide whether to use the self-assessment sheet for children to record their achievements and next steps.

Teacher support
Less confident learners: Remind these children that *quadrilateral* means 'four-sided shape'. Also remind them of the term *adjacent*.
More confident learners: Encourage these children to quiz each other, describing shapes using the properties set out on the display pages.

Common misconceptions
Children don't easily recognise shapes such as parallelograms and rhombuses as irregular quadrilaterals.
Explain that a regular shape has all sides and angles equal, so the only regular quadrilateral is a square. Ask children to draw various quadrilaterals to test this.

Probing questions
● Which shapes have diagonals that dissect at right angles?
● Which shapes have diagonals of equal length?

Next steps
Support: Reinforce this activity by focusing on other regular polygons, such as pentagons and hexagons. Refer back to Year 5 Block B Unit 3.
Extension: Extend this activity to investigating parallel and perpendicular faces in 3D solids. Refer also to Year 6 Block B Unit 2.

Activities ⑧ and ⑨

Prior learning	Framework objective
Children understand the terms face, edge, vertex, vertices. They can identify and describe the properties of 3D solids.	Make and draw shapes with increasing accuracy and apply knowledge of their properties
	Vocabulary face, edge, vertex, vertices, parallel, perpendicular, net, flap, prism
	Resources **Worksheet:** In the net **Resource sheets:** Properties of 3D solids, Self-assessment **Classroom resources:** set-squares, a range of 3D solids (cube, cuboid, cylinder, triangular prism, square-based pyramid, triangular-based pyramid)

⑧ Properties of 3D solids

Carry out this activity in small groups. Hold up a range of different 3D solids and ask questions about their properties. For example, hold up a hexagonal prism and ask: *How many vertices does this shape have?* In addition, ask questions that require children to identify solids (you can use the resource sheet 'Properties of 3D solids' for this purpose). Decide whether to use the self-assessment sheet for the children to record their achievements and what they need to do next.

Teacher support
Less confident learners: Start by modelling the description of a cube using vertices, edges and faces, and referring to parallel and perpendicular faces.
More confident learners: Allow the children to look at and handle each solid. Then remove them before asking questions, so that they have to visualise them.

Common misconceptions
Children confuse 2D and 3D shape vocabulary (for example, using 'angle' and 'side' rather than 'vertex' and 'face').
Show both types of shape and run through the differences in vocabulary.

Some children may forget to count the faces or edges they cannot see.
Encourage these children to imagine the solid floating in the air so that they can see all around it, or give actual solid shapes so they can identify the properties.

Probing questions
● How would you describe a cone and a sphere?
● What makes these shapes different to the other 3D solids we looked at?

Next steps
Support: Limit the investigation of how many different nets will make an open or a closed cube. Refer back to Year 5 Block B Unit 3.
Extension: Ask children to investigate the nets of other solid shapes, such as triangular or hexagonal prisms. Refer also to Year 6 Block B Unit 2.

⑨ In the net

Hand out the worksheet 'In the net'. Ask the children to finish drawing incomplete nets and draw the net of a square-based pyramid.

Teacher support
Less confident learners: If possible, provide a set of Polydron, Clixi or similar equipment for these children. They can then build each solid before attempting to draw the net.
More confident learners: Encourage these children to draw the more difficult nets (the choice of net often indicates the child's level of confidence).

Common misconceptions
Children find it hard to visualise a solid shape in a 2D plane.
Use Polydron or Clixi to demonstrate how a solid will look if 'opened up'.

When adding flaps to the shape, children find it difficult to visualise which face the flaps attach to.
It may be necessary for children to build a net without flaps initially. Fold into the solid shape and then mark where the flaps should be. With practice, the ability to visualise where faces will meet will improve.

Probing questions
● What is the minimum number of flaps needed to secure a cube/triangular prism/square-based pyramid so that every edge is sealed?
● Can any of the solids be put together to make another solid? (For example, two square-based pyramids stuck base to base will make an octahedron.)

Next steps
Support: Move from nets of cubes, to nets of square- and triangular-based pyramids. Review how children draw the faces so that they fit together. Refer to Year 5 Block B Unit 3.
Extension: Challenge children to create nets for a dodecahedron and an icosahedron. Refer also to Year 6 Block B Unit 2.

Unit 2 Securing number facts, understanding shape

Introduction

This nine-lesson block gives prominence to securing number facts in a range of contexts. Children investigate multiples, factors, primes and prime factors, and use these to solve number problems. They continue to explore patterns, relationships and properties of number, and use a range of methods to check results. They consolidate mental methods of multiplication and division facts in the context of decimals. In addition, the unit includes activities where children describe and identify parallel and perpendicular edges and faces to classify 2D and 3D shapes. They practise drawing shapes with accuracy, using knowledge of their properties.

Framework objectives	Assessment focuses		Success criteria for Year 6	Learning outcomes
	Level 5	Level 4		
① Symbol value				
Represent and interpret sequences, patterns and relationships involving numbers and shapes; suggest and test hypotheses; construct and use simple expressions and formulae in words then symbols (for example the cost of *c* pens at 15 pence each is 15*c* pence)	• draw simple conclusions of their own and give an explanation of their reasoning, e.g. • identify more complex patterns, making generalisations in words and begin to express generalisations using symbolic notation • use examples and counter-examples to justify conclusions • construct, express in symbolic form, and use simple formulae involving one or two operations	• search for a solution by trying out ideas of their own, e.g. • identify patterns as they work and form their own generalisations/rules in words • begin to use simple formulae expressed in words	• works in an organised way when solving problems • can explain methods used when presenting a solution to a problem • can identify more complex patterns and is beginning to express these patterns using symbols instead of numbers	*I can describe and explain sequences, patterns and relationships.* *I can suggest hypotheses and test them.* *I can write and use simple expressions in words and formulae.*
② How many?				
Tabulate systematically the information in a problem or puzzle; identify and record the steps or calculations needed to solve it, using symbols where appropriate; interpret solutions in the original context and check their accuracy	• show understanding of situations by describing them mathematically using symbols, words and diagrams, e.g. • organise their work from the outset, looking for ways to record systematically • decide how best to represent conclusions, using appropriate recording • begin to understand and use formulae and symbols to represent problems • check results, considering whether these are reasonable, e.g. • check as they work, spotting and correcting errors and reviewing methods	• present information and results in a clear and organised way, e.g. • organise written work, e.g. record results in order • begin to work in an organised way from the start • consider appropriate units • use related vocabulary accurately • develop own strategies for solving problems, e.g. • check answers and ensure solutions make sense in the context of the problem • review their work and approaches	• organises work systematically so that errors can be easily recognised • refers to the context of the problem to ensure they have reached the solution that was required • recognises the information that is important to solve a problem, and indicates which information is not relevant • decides how to present solutions and conclusions, using a range of strategies and recording methods	*I can use a table to help me solve a problem.* *I can identify and record what I need to do to solve the problem, checking that my answer makes sense and is accurate.*

Unit 2 Securing number facts, understanding shape

Framework objectives	Assessment focuses		Success criteria for Year 6	Learning outcomes
	Level 5	Level 4		
③ Use your squares				
Use knowledge of multiplication facts to derive quickly squares of numbers to 12 × 12 and the corresponding squares of multiples of 10	There is no assessment focus for this level	• recognise and describe number relationships including multiple, factor and square	• makes connections to previous work relating to multiples and squares; is able to use this work to help find answers in new situations • uses sensible approximations in order to estimate the answers to written problems	I can say the squares of numbers to 12 × 12 and work out the squares of multiples of 10.
④ Sports day				
Use knowledge of place value and multiplication facts to 10 × 10 to derive related multiplication and division facts involving decimals (e.g. 0.8 × 7, 4.8 ÷ 6)	• use all four operations with decimals to two places, e.g. • multiply or divide decimal numbers by a single digit, e.g. 31.62 × 7	• multiply a simple decimal by a single digit, e.g. • calculate 36.2 × 8 • quickly derive division facts that correspond to multiplication facts up to 10 × 10	• knows times tables to 10 × 10, and each associated division fact • uses knowledge of tables and place value to work out calculations with multiples of 10, e.g. 40 × 8, 240 ÷ 6 • uses an efficient written method to multiply or divide a simple decimal by a single digit	I can use table facts to work out related facts with decimals.
⑤ Use your primes				
Recognise that prime numbers have only two factors and identify prime numbers less than 100; find the prime factors of two-digit numbers	• recognise and use number patterns and relationships, e.g. • find two-digit prime numbers	• recognise and describe number relationships including multiple, factor and square	• understands and can find prime factors of two-digit numbers • is beginning to use prime factors to multiply two-digit numbers by two-digit numbers • finds numbers that share the same prime factor	I can work out which numbers less than 100 are prime.
⑥ Sort it				
Use approximations, inverse operations and tests of divisibility to estimate and check results	• approximate to check answers to problems are of the correct magnitude • check solutions by applying inverse operations or estimating using approximations • check results, considering whether these are reasonable, e.g. • check as they work, spotting and correcting errors and reviewing methods	• check the reasonableness of results with reference to the context or size of numbers • develop own strategies for solving problems, e.g. • check answers and ensure solutions make sense in the context of the problem • review their work and approaches	• knows the tests of divisibility for 2, 5, 10, 3, 6, 9, 4 and 8 • uses these tests to work out if given numbers will divide by various divisors	I can estimate and check the result of a calculation.

Unit 2 ▢ Securing number facts, understanding shape

Framework objectives	Assessment focuses		Success criteria for Year 6	Learning outcomes
	Level 5	Level 4		
⑦ Calculators allowed				
Use a calculator to solve problems involving multi-step calculations	• use a calculator where appropriate to calculate fractions/percentages of quantities/measurements, e.g. • find fractions of quantities such as $3/8$ of 980 • find percentages such as 15% of 360g	• use inverse operations, e.g. • use a calculator and inverse operations to find missing numbers, including decimals • solve problems with or without a calculator	• chooses when a calculator is more appropriate than mental or written methods • uses a calculator to solve number problems, using inverse operations to check results • understands how the order of what is keyed into a calculator can affect the solution to a problem • understands that measurements must be keyed into their calculator using the same units	*I can use a calculator to solve problems with more than one step.*
⑧ Corner to corner				
Describe, identify and visualise parallel and perpendicular edges or faces; use these properties to classify 2D shapes and 3D solids	• use a wider range of properties of 2D and 3D shapes, e.g. • understand 'parallel' and begin to understand 'perpendicular' in relation to edges or faces	• use the properties of 2D and 3D shapes	• can identify similarities and differences between similar shapes • understands the term diagonal and knows how many diagonals common quadrilaterals have • can describe shapes that have diagonals that intersect at right angles	*I can use the properties of parallel and perpendicular to describe and classify 2D shapes and 3D solids.*
⑨ Drawing shapes				
Make and draw shapes with increasing accuracy and apply knowledge of their properties	• use a wider range of properties of 2D and 3D shapes, e.g. • draw a parallelogram or trapezium of a given area on a square grid • reason about shapes, positions and movements, e.g. • draw shapes with a fixed number of lines of symmetry	• use the properties of 2D and 3D shapes • make 3D models by linking given faces or edges • draw common 2D shapes in different orientations on grids, e.g. • complete a rectangle which has two sides drawn at an oblique angle to the grid	• can draw a range of quadrilaterals using rulers, set-squares and protractors • can give instructions to others that are clear and concise, on how to draw a range of quadrilaterals with given properties, e.g. a regular trapezium, a rhombus	*I can make and draw shapes accurately.*

BLOCK B

Activity ①

Prior learning
Children can use symbols to stand for unknown numbers.

Framework objective
Represent and interpret sequences, patterns and relationships involving numbers and shapes; suggest and test hypotheses; construct and use simple expressions and formulae in words then symbols (for example the cost of *c* pens at 15 pence each is 15*c* pence)

Vocabulary
sequence, pattern, generalise, reasoning, predict, rule, formula, relationship, term, value

Resources
Worksheet: Symbol value
Classroom resources: calculators

① Symbol value

Hand out copies of the worksheet 'Symbol value'. Children are asked to find the value of the symbols by working out the relationships between the symbols and the numbers given.

Teacher support
Less confident learners: Encourage these children to rewrite each calculation in section 1 in full, putting in all the given information before attempting to find the missing numbers. Remind them how to use the inverse operation in preparation for section 2.
More confident learners: Quickly move these children on to section 2, which requires the use of a calculator and asks them to explain their reasoning.

Common misconceptions
Children are not confident with using the inverse operation, or are unsure of the operations to use.
Give some simple examples, such as $15 \times ? = 60$, so divide 60 by 15 to find the answer; $168 \div ? = 14$, so divide 168 by 14 to find the answer.

Probing questions
● How can you use symbols to help you solve number problems?
● Are there times when you cannot use inverse operations? Can you give an example?

Next steps
Support: Provide opportunities for children to work in pairs to create their own symbol problems. They should swap with another pair and try to solve each others' problems. Refer back to Year 6 Block B Unit 1.
Extension: Provide opportunities for children to create problems involving decimals that need to be solved using a calculator. Refer also to Year 6 Block B Unit 3.

Activity ②

Prior learning
Children can organise information in a table.

Framework objective
Tabulate systematically the information in a problem or puzzle; identify and record the steps or calculations needed to solve it, using symbols where appropriate; interpret solutions in the original context and check their accuracy

Vocabulary
tabulate, hypothesise, systematically, predict, statement

Resources
Worksheet: How many?

② How many?

Hand out copies of the worksheet 'How many?'. The children have a choice of three tasks to undertake, all of which require them to set out information in a systematic way:
● Task 1 is to list all the possible combinations that can be made from five digits.
● Task 2 is to identify the number of rectangles in a given shape.
● Task 3 is to organise information to find out the rule for a growing number pattern.

Teacher support
Less confident learners: These children should undertake tasks 1 and 2, which require the organisation and checking of information, but not the construction of a table to record results.
More confident learners: These children should undertake tasks 2 and 3. The third task requires a multi-step approach in order to correctly identify the pattern.

Common misconceptions
Children are not systematic in their approach, randomly recording their findings. Encourage children to record in an organised manner. For example, in task 1 they should make all the numbers possible using 1 as the starting digit. Then repeat, using 3 as the starting digit.

Probing questions
● How can you organise your information so that you are sure all possible solutions are included?
● How can you make sure you have not missed out any information?

Next steps
Support: Provide further practice at investigating systematically, by posing questions relating to number squares. Refer back to Year 6 Block B Unit 1.
Extension: Extend the above activity to include predicting numbers in patterns that continue outside the number grid given. Refer also to Year 6 Block B Unit 3.

BLOCK B

BLOCK B

Activity ③

Prior learning Children can instantly recall tables to 10 ×10. They know the square numbers up to 12 × 12 and they know the corresponding squares of multiples of 10.	**Framework objective** Use knowledge of multiplication facts to derive quickly squares of numbers to 12 × 12 and the corresponding squares of multiples of 10 **Vocabulary** square number, multiple, consecutive, product, estimate **Resources** **Worksheet:** Use your squares

③ Use your squares

Hand out copies of the worksheet 'Use your squares'. The children are required to use their knowledge of square numbers and squares of multiples of 10 to solve some word problems.

Teacher support
Less confident learners: Remind these children how to round to the nearest 10 or 100 in order to aid their estimating of the answer.
More confident learners: Provide these children with some word problems involving decimal numbers for them to solve.

Common misconceptions
Children are confident in squaring single-digit numbers, but are uncertain as to the place value involved when squaring multiples of 10.
Encourage children to check that the number of zeros in the answer matches the number of zeros in the calculation. For example, 50 × 50 has two zeros, so there must be two zeros in answer (2500).

Probing questions
● How could you use 15 × 15 = 225 to find 15 × 16?
● What number multiplied by itself gives the answer 900?

Next steps
Support: Give the children further word problems to solve, particularly ones involving multiples of 10. Refer back to Year 6 Block B Unit 1.
Extension: Provide children wtih the task of investigating what squares of multiples of 10 lie between 1000 and 2000. Encourage them to construct word problems involving the square roots of these numbers. Refer also to Year 6 Block B Unit 3.

Activity ④

Prior learning
Children can recall the table facts to 10 ×10 and can relate these facts to decimal numbers. For example, 7 × 6 = 42, so 7 × 0.6 = 4.2 and 6 × 9 = 54, so 0.6 × 0.9 = 0.54.

Framework objective
Use knowledge of place value and multiplication facts to 10 × 10 to derive related multiplication and division facts involving decimals

Vocabulary
decimal, multiple, factor, place value, digit

Resources
Worksheet: Sports day

④ Sports day

Provide the children with copies of the worksheet 'Sports day'. In this activity they are asked to solve word problems using their knowledge of multiplication facts and the associated division facts.

Teacher support
Less confident learners: Revise how to find related facts involving decimals when starting with a whole number calculation first. For example, 5 × 9 = 45, so 0.5 × 9 = 4.5, and 0.5 × 0.9 = 0.45.
More confident learners: Encourage these children to generate their own number problems for their partner to investigate.

Common misconceptions
Some children may have difficulty in completing division facts correctly. They write the calculation in the incorrect order (for example, 7 ÷ 4.2 = 0.6 instead of 4.2 ÷ 7).
Tell the children to visualise what the number sentence would be like if there were no decimal numbers in it. They could then be reminded that the largest number (the dividend) must be written first in a division sum.

Probing questions
● What number multiplied by 8 equals 7.2?
● What happens when you multiply a decimal by a decimal?

Next steps
Support: Provide further practice at deriving multiplication and division facts relating to decimals. Refer back to Year 6 Block B Unit 1.
Extension: Ask children to investigate what happens when a whole number is multiplied by a decimal and when a whole number is divided by a decimal. What do they notice? Refer also to Year 6 Block B Unit 3.

Activity ⑤

Prior learning
Children can identify pairs of factors of two-digit whole numbers.

Framework objective
Recognise that prime numbers have only two factors and identify prime numbers less than 100; find the prime factors of two-digit numbers

Vocabulary
factor, prime, prime factor, multiple

Resources
Worksheet: Use your primes
Classroom resources: multiplication squares (for support)

⑤ Use your primes

Give out copies of the worksheet 'Use your primes'. The children need to use prime factors to help them to multiply a two-digit number by a two-digit number.

Teacher support
Less confident learners: Make multiplication squares available and remind these children how to be systematic when finding the factors. Remind them to use jottings to help them with the multiplication of the prime factors.
More confident learners: Encourage these children to multiply the prime factors mentally, using the minimal amount of jottings.

Common misconceptions
Children start with the smallest numbers when multiplying, then are left with quite large numbers to multiply by the prime factors of 5 or 7.
Encourage children to write out the prime factors in order.

Probing questions
● When multiplying the prime factors, which of the factors is it best to start with? (Elicit that the larger numbers should be multiplied first, as by leaving the 2s to the end of the multiplication they only need to call on their doubling skills.)
● What other methods can you use to multiply a two-digit number by a two-digit number?

Next steps
Support: Provide further practice in using prime factors to find the product of a two-digit number multiplied by a two-digit number. Refer back to Year 6 Block B Unit 1.
Extension: Challenge the children to use prime factors to multiply a three-digit number by two-digit numbers. Refer also to Year 6 Block B Unit 3.

Activity ⑥

Prior learning
Children understand the terms tests of divisibility, approximate and inverse operation. They can round integers to the nearest 10, 100 or 1000, and decimals to the nearest whole number.

Framework objective
Use approximations, tests of divisibility and inverse operations to estimate and check results

Vocabulary
integer, decimal, round, estimate, approximate, inverse, divisibility, operation

Resources
Interactive activity: Sort it

⑥ Sort it

Reveal the interactive activity 'Sort it'. In this activity, the children are required to drag different numbers into the correct set, using their knowledge of tests of divisibility.

Teacher support
Less confident learners: Focus on the sets that require children to know the tests for divisibility by 3, 4 and 5.
More confident learners: Quickly move on to those numbers which require knowledge of the tests for divisibility by 6, 8 and 9.

Common misconceptions
Children look at the last digit in the given number and assume that if it is not in the table they are investigating, then it is not divisible by that number.
Remind these children that this only applies to the 5-times and 10-times tables. Go through other divisibility rules with them to remind them of their error.

Probing questions
● Is a number that is divisible by 3 always divisible by 6 and by 9? Explain your reasoning.
● Why must a number that is divisible by 8 always be an even number?

Next steps
Support: Move children on to tests of divisibility for the 6-times, 8-times and 9-times tables. Refer back to Year 6 Block B Unit 1.
Extension: Challenge the children to find the test of divisibility for the 11-times table. It is clear for two-digit numbers, but challenging for three-digit numbers. (Rule: add the first and last digit. If they equal the middle digit, the number is divisible by 11 – for example, 253.) Refer also to Year 6 Block B Unit 3.

BLOCK B

BLOCK B

Activity ⑦

Prior learning
Children can competently use a calculator, and they know how to clear the memory should it be activated.

Framework objective
Use a calculator to solve problems involving multi-step calculations

Vocabulary
problem, solution, calculate, reasoning, method, inverse, operation, product

Resources
Worksheet: Calculators allowed
Classroom resources: calculators

⑦ Calculators allowed

Provide each child with a copy of the worksheet 'Calculators allowed'. In this activity the children are required to solve one-step and two-step calculations and word problems.

Teacher support
Less confident learners: Encourage these children to make jottings of the operations they have carried out, so that they do not forget which buttons they have pressed.
More confident learners: These children could move straight to questions 7–12 on the worksheet. These questions contain two-step problems, for which they could use the memory function of the calculator if they are secure with its use.

Common misconceptions
Some children are not secure in entering information into a calculator.
Remind these children of the need to change the units of measurement so that they are common within the problem. For example, if working with money, 32p should be entered as 0.32 if working in pounds. Similarly, when reading answers, 30p will appear as 0.3 and 3p as 0.03.

Probing questions
● In what order did you have to work out this calculation?
● Explain how you decided which missing digits had to be used to solve the problem.
● What was your estimation for this problem that helped you find the answer?

Next steps
Support: Provide more opportunities for calculator work, especially multi-step problems. Refer back to Year 5 Block B Unit 3.
Extension: Remind the children how to use the memory function effectively, and provide a range of problems for them to practise using it. Refer to Year 6 Block B Unit 3.

Activity ⑧

BLOCK B

Prior learning
Children know the difference between a trapezium, a kite, a rhombus and a parallelogram.

Framework objective
Describe, identify and visualise parallel and perpendicular edges or faces; use these properties to classify 2D shapes and 3D solids

Vocabulary
parallel, perpendicular, diagonal, angle, intersect, trapezium, kite, rhombus, parallelogram, quadrilateral

Resources
Worksheet: Corner to corner
Classroom resources: protractors, rulers

⑧ Corner to corner

Hand out copies of the worksheet 'Corner to corner'. Children are asked to draw the diagonals on a set of quadrilaterals, then investigate a range of properties, such as:
- Which diagonals intersect at right angles?
- Which diagonals are perpendicular?
- Which angles in each quadrilateral are equal?

Teacher support
Less confident learners: Some children may not be confident in using a protractor. They may need to be reminded about this.
More confident learners: Set these children the task of investigating the diagonals of larger polygons such as pentagons and hexagons.

Common misconceptions
Some children confuse diagonals with lines of symmetry, and draw lines across the shape that are not from angle to angle.
Recap on the difference so that the children are clear about this before they start the activity.

Probing questions
- Which shapes have diagonals that intersect at the mid point of the shape?
- Which shapes have diagonals of equal length?

Next steps
Support: Extend the above activity to other regular polygons. Refer back to Year 6 Block B Unit 1.
Extension: Extend this activity to investigating lines of symmetry in polygons, looking for the relationship between the number of sides and the number of lines of symmetry. Refer also to Year 6 Block B Unit 3.

BLOCK B

Activity ⑨

Prior learning
Children can measure accurately to within 2mm when using a ruler. They can use a protractor to draw angles within 5° of accuracy.

Framework objective
Make and draw shapes with increasing accuracy and apply knowledge of their properties

Vocabulary
right angle, degree, set square, names of 2D shapes

Resources
Resource sheet: Self-assessment
Classroom resources: centimetre-squared paper, plain paper, pencils, protractors, rulers, set-squares

⑨ Drawing shapes

Carry out this activity in small groups, with a teaching assistant or teacher. Ask the children to draw shapes on their squared paper, using set criteria and a range of equipment. Take particular note of the appropriateness of the equipment the children choose to use. Below are some ideas of shapes that the children could draw:
- a pentagon that has three right angles
- a regular trapezium with a base of 8cm and two acute angles of 60°
- a kite with diagonals of 9cm and 5cm
- a rhombus with an angle of 60°
- a parallelogram with acute angles of 70° and obtuse angles of 110°

Decide whether to use the self-assessment sheet for the children to record their achievements and what they need to do next.

Teacher support
Less confident learners: These children may need to use centimetre-squared paper to draw their shapes. In addition, the questions posed may need to focus on side length rather than angle size.
More confident learners: Have these children use plain paper so that they need to rely on choosing the correct equipment to draw angles accurately (for example, a set-square for right angles).

Common misconceptions
Some children may not be confident in choosing the correct equipment.
Remind these children of the function of a set-square and when it would be used in preference to a protractor. Some children may also need to be reminded where to start measuring when using a ruler, as some rulers start at the edge while others have a small lead-in space.

Probing questions
- How would you draw a rhombus using a ruler and protractor?
- Is it possible to draw a trapezium with two right angles?
- Give me instructions for how to draw an equilateral triangle.

Next steps
Support: Give extra practice at drawing shapes using the range of equipment as detailed above. Refer back to Year 6 Block B Unit 1.
Extension: Challenge children to construct regular polygons such as a pentagon and a hexagon, using a ruler and a protractor. Refer also to Year 6 Block B Unit 3.

Unit 3 Securing number facts, understanding shape

Introduction
This block focuses upon securing number facts in a range of contexts. Children use number facts and place value to solve multi-step word problems involving whole numbers and decimals. They explore patterns and relationships in number, and use approximations and tests of divisibility to check results. They use inverse operations to solve problems. In addition, children extend work on properties of shapes, classifying 3D shapes using criteria relating to parallel and perpendicular faces and sides. They explore the relationship between the number of edges, faces and sides in a polyhedron. They draw and make shapes with accuracy, using a range of equipment.

Framework objectives	Assessment focuses		Success criteria for Year 6	Learning outcomes
	Level 5	Level 4		
(1) Growing patterns				
Represent and interpret sequences, patterns and relationships involving numbers and shapes; suggest and test hypotheses; construct and use simple expressions and formulae in words then symbols	● draw simple conclusions of their own and give an explanation of their reasoning, e.g. ● identify more complex patterns, making generalisations in words and begin to express generalisations using symbolic notation ● use examples and counter-examples to justify conclusions ● construct, express in symbolic form, and use simple formulae involving one or two operations	● search for a solution by trying out ideas of their own, e.g. ● identify patterns as they work and form their own generalisations/rules in words ● begin to use simple formulae expressed in words	● can continue patterns in shape sequences, drawing the next terms ● is able to describe patterns by using appropriate vocabulary ● is beginning to use symbols to express simple number sentences ● can explain how to find the tenth/ hundredth of any given term in a sequence	*I can describe and explain sequences, patterns and relationships.* *I can suggest hypotheses and test them.* *I can write and use simple expressions in words and formulae.*
(2) Order! Order!				
Tabulate systematically the information in a problem or puzzle; identify and record the steps or calculations needed to solve it, using symbols where appropriate; interpret solutions in the original context and check their accuracy	● show understanding of situations by describing them mathematically using symbols, words and diagrams, e.g. ● organise their work from the outset, looking for ways to record systematically ● decide how best to represent conclusions, using appropriate recording ● begin to understand and use formulae and symbols to represent problems ● check results, considering whether these are reasonable, e.g. ● check as they work, spotting and correcting errors and reviewing methods	● present information and results in a clear and organised way, e.g. ● organise written work, e.g. record results in order ● begin to work in an organised way from the start ● consider appropriate units ● use related vocabulary accurately ● check answers and ensure solutions make sense in the context of the problem ● review their work and approaches	● organises workings systematically so that calculations can be checked for errors ● can identify the information needed to carry out a task ● is able to break a problem down into smaller steps	*I can use a table to help me solve a problem.* *I can identify and record what I need to do to solve the problem, checking that my answer makes sense and is accurate.*

Unit 3 📖 Securing number facts, understanding shape

Framework objectives	Assessment focuses		Success criteria for Year 6	Learning outcomes
	Level 5	Level 4		
③ All square				
Use knowledge of multiplication facts to derive quickly squares of numbers to 12 × 12 and the corresponding squares of multiples of 10	There is no assessment focus for this level	• recognise and describe number relationships including multiple, factor and square	• uses knowledge of square numbers to find the square of any multiple of 10 up to 10,000	*I can say the squares of numbers to 12 × 12 and work out the squares of multiples of 10.*
④ Right or wrong?				
Use knowledge of place value and multiplication facts to 10 × 10 to derive related multiplication and division facts involving decimals (e.g. 0.8 × 7, 4.8 ÷ 6)	• use all four operations with decimals to two places, e.g. • multiply or divide decimal numbers by a single digit, e.g. 31.62 × 7	• multiply a simple decimal by a single digit, e.g. • calculate 36.2 × 8 • quickly derive division facts that correspond to multiplication facts up to 10 × 10	• knows times tables to 10 × 10, and each associated fact • is able to use their table knowledge and place value, to work out calculations • uses an efficient written method to multiply or divide a simple decimal by a single digit	*I can use the times tables to work out decimal facts such as 0.4 × 8 and 5.6 ÷ 7.*
⑤ Prime investigation				
Recognise that prime numbers have only two factors and identify prime numbers less than 100; find the prime factors of two-digit numbers	• recognise and use number patterns and relationships, e.g. • find two-digit prime numbers	• recognise and describe number relationships including multiple, factor and square	• explains what a prime factor is and gives the prime factors of two-digit numbers • suggests a way of investigating which numbers up to 30 have only one prime factor • uses information gained about prime factors of numbers up to 30 to predict which numbers between 30 and 60 will also have only one distinct prime factor	*I can tell you all the prime numbers up to 100 and find the prime factors of other numbers.*

Unit 3 ▢ Securing number facts, understanding shape

Framework objectives	Assessment focuses		Success criteria for Year 6	Learning outcomes
	Level 5	Level 4		
⑥ Is it correct?				

Use approximations, inverse operations and tests of divisibility to estimate and check results	• approximate to check answers to problems are of the correct magnitude
	• check solutions by applying inverse operations or estimating using approximations
	• check results, considering whether these are reasonable, e.g.
	  • check as they work, spotting and correcting errors and reviewing methods
		• check the reasonableness of results with reference to the context or size of numbers
		• develop own strategies for solving problems, e.g.
		  • check answers and ensure solutions make sense in the context of the problem
		  • review their work and approaches
			• is able to approximate before solving a problem, then uses the approximation to check the reasonableness of the answer
			• can break a problem up into several steps
			• recognises the information that is important to solve a problem and indicates which information is not relevant
			• checks their answers as they work, correcting errors
				I can estimate and check the result of a calculation.

⑦ Know your calculator				

Use a calculator to solve problems involving multi-step calculations	• use a calculator where appropriate to calculate fractions/percentages of quantities/measurements, e.g.
	  • find fractions of quantities such as 3/8 of 980
	  • find percentages such as 15% of 360g
		• use inverse operations, e.g.
		  • use a calculator and inverse operations to find missing numbers, including decimals
		• solve problems with or without a calculator
			• uses a calculator effectively to solve two-step problems, choosing appropriate operations
			• can decide whether mental, written or calculator methods are most appropriate when given a range of written problems
			• can interpret a calculator display in terms of measurement
				I can use a calculator to solve problems with more than one step.

⑧ Shape sorting				
Describe, identify and visualise parallel and perpendicular edges or faces; use these properties to classify 2D shapes and 3D solids	• use a wider range of properties of 2D and 3D shapes, eg • understand 'parallel' and begin to understand 'perpendicular' in relation to edges or faces	• use the properties of 2D and 3D shapes	• can sort 3D solids in the context of faces that are parallel or perpendicular • uses the correct terminology when describing shapes • knows how to sort into a two-criteria Carroll diagram	*I can identify 3D shapes with perpendicular or parallel edges or faces.*
⑨ Drawing circles				
Make and draw shapes with increasing accuracy and apply knowledge of their properties	• use a wider range of properties of 2D/3D shapes, e.g. • draw a parallelogram or trapezium of a given area on a square grid • reason about shapes, positions and movements	• use the properties of 2D and 3D shapes • make 3D models by linking given faces or edges • draw common 2D shapes in different orientations on grids	• can use compasses with precision • understands the terms radius, diameter and circumference	*I can make and draw shapes accurately.*

BLOCK B

Activity ①

BLOCK B

Prior learning
Children can organise information in a table.

Framework objective
Represent and interpret sequences, patterns and relationships involving numbers and shapes; suggest and test hypotheses; construct and use simple expressions and formulae in words then symbols (for example, the cost of *c* pens at 15 pence each is 15*c* pence)

Vocabulary
sequence, pattern, generalise, reasoning, predict, rule, formula, relationship, term, value

Resources
Worksheet: Growing patterns

① Growing patterns

Hand out copies of the worksheet 'Growing patterns'. In this activity the children are asked to investigate sequences of shapes, working out terms in the sequences and describing ways in which the patterns grow.

Teacher support
Less confident learners: Remind these children to use jottings, writing down the number of shapes in each pattern and looking at the differences between them.
More confident learners: Encourage these children to write out the growing patterns as number sentences, using symbols to stand for the number of each term.

Common misconceptions
Children can visualise the pattern but are unable to express how it grows.
Demonstrate how to write a growing sequence. For example, a sequence that starts with four squares, then adds three more for each term, would be written as $3n + 1$, where n = the number of the term in the sequence.

Probing questions
● Describe this sequence to me. How many squares/crosses would be in the 10th term?
● Is there a quick way to work out the 100th term or do you have to count through all 99 terms?

Next steps
Support: Provide opportunities for children to create their own growing patterns to try out on partners. Refer back to Year 6 Block B Unit 2.
Extension: Provide further opportunities for children to construct simple expressions and formulae from number and shape patterns. Refer also to the Year 6 extension or Year 7 material if appropriate.

Unit 3 Securing number facts, understanding shape

Activity ②

Prior learning
Children can organise information in a table.

Framework objective
Tabulate systematically the information in a problem or puzzle; identify and record the steps or calculations needed to solve it, using symbols where appropriate; interpret solutions in the original context and check their accuracy

Vocabulary
tabulate, hypothesise, systematically, predict, statement

Resources
Worksheet: Order! Order!
Classroom resources: Multi-link (for support)

② Order! Order!

Hand out copies of the worksheet 'Order! Order!'. In this activity the children need to find ways of combining given information, by listing systematically or producing a table or chart.

Teacher support
Less confident learners: Encourage these children to take a practical approach to checking combinations – for example, by drawing or using coloured pencils to show all possible answers.
More confident learners: Encourage these children to design their own tables or charts, perhaps using symbols or abbreviations to record results.

Common misconceptions
Children are not systematic in their approach, randomly recording their findings. Encourage children to record in an organised manner. For example, when working out the colour combinations for the scarf, make all the combinations using red first, then blue, and so on.

Probing questions
● How can you organise your information so that you are sure all possible solutions are included?
● How can you make sure you have not missed out any information?

Next steps
Support: Provide further practice in investigating systematically – for example, by using Multi-link to create growing shapes. Refer back to Year 6 Block B Unit 2.
Extension: Extend the activity to include patterns that grow in more than one dimension. Refer also to the Year 6 extension or Year 7 material if appropriate.

BLOCK B

BLOCK B

Activity ③

Prior learning
Children can instantly recall multiplication tables to 10 ×10. They know the square numbers up to 12 × 12 and the corresponding squares of multiples of 10.

Framework objective
Use knowledge of multiplication facts to derive quickly squares of numbers to 12 × 12 and the corresponding squares of multiples of 10

Vocabulary
square, number, multiple, consecutive, product, estimate

Resources
Worksheet: All square

③ All square

Give out the worksheet 'All square'. The children are required to use their knowledge of square numbers and squares of multiples of 10 to investigate square numbers up to 10,000.

Teacher support
Less confident learners: Recap on the place value aspect when squaring multiples of 10. Ask: *How many zeros would be needed in the answer?*
More confident learners: Quickly move children on to question 2, where they are asked to find the squares of multiples up to 10,000.

Common misconceptions
Children are confident in squaring single-digit numbers, but are uncertain as to the place value involved when squaring multiples of 10.
Encourage children to check that the number of zeros in the answer matches the number of zeros in the calculation. For example, 50 × 50 has two zeros, so there must be two zeros in the answer (2500).

Probing questions
● If you know how many square numbers there are between 1 and 100, will this help to find out how many square numbers are between 1 and 1000? What about between 1 and 10,000?
● What number multiplied by itself gives the answer 1600?

Next steps
Support: Challenge children to create word problems involving square numbers up to 1000. Refer back to Year 6 Block B Unit 2.
Extension: Challenge children to create word problems involving square numbers up to 10,000. Refer also to the Year 6 extension or Year 7 material if appropriate.

Activity ④

BLOCK B

Prior learning
Children can recall all table facts to 10 × 10. They can relate these facts to decimal numbers, for example: 7 × 6 = 42, so 7 × 0.6 = 4.2; and 6 × 9 = 54, so 0.6 × 0.9 = 0.54.

Framework objective
Use knowledge of place value and multiplication facts to 10 × 10 to derive related multiplication and division facts involving decimals (for example, 0.8 × 7, 4.8 ÷ 6)

Vocabulary
decimal, multiple, factor, place, value, digit

Resources
Worksheet: Right or wrong?

④ Right or wrong?

Hand out copies of the worksheet 'Right or wrong?'. The children have to use their knowledge of multiplication facts and the associated division facts to select the correct solution to each calculation.

Teacher support
Less confident learners: Revise how to find related facts involving decimals when starting with a whole number calculation first. For example: 5 × 9 = 45, so 0.5 × 9 = 4.5, and 0.5 × 0.9 = 0.45.
More confident learners: Ask these children to explain their reasoning to show how they calculated the correct solution for each problem.

Common misconceptions
Some children may have difficulty in completing division facts correctly - for example, writing the calculation in the incorrect order, 7 ÷ 4.2 = 0.6 instead of 4.2 ÷ 7.
Tell the children to visualise what the number sentence would be like if there were no decimal numbers in it. Then remind them that the largest number (the dividend) must be written first in a division calculation.

Probing questions
● Explain how you worked out the correct answer.
● How did your tables help you with multiplying and dividing decimal numbers?

Next steps
Support: Provide further practice at deriving multiplication and division facts relating to decimals. Refer back to Year 6 Block B Unit 2.
Extension: Ask children to write their own word problems involving money, measures and numbers to match given calculations (for example, 3.6 ÷ 0.9). Refer also to the Year 6 extension or Year 7 material if appropriate.

Activity ⑤

Prior learning Children can identify pairs of factors of two-digit whole numbers.	**Framework objective** Recognise that prime numbers have only two factors and identify prime numbers less than 100; find the prime factors of two-digit numbers **Vocabulary** factor, prime, prime factor, multiple, distinct, prime factor **Resources** **Worksheet:** Prime investigation **Classroom resources:** multiplication squares (for support)

⑤ Prime investigation

Give out copies of the worksheet 'Prime investigation'. The children are asked to investigate which numbers up to 30 have only one distinct prime factor, then use this to predict how many more numbers there will be with just one distinct prime factor between 30 and 60.

Teacher support
Less confident learners: Make multiplication squares available and remind these children how to be systematic about finding the factors. Remind them to use jottings to help them with the multiplication of the prime factors.
More confident learners: Encourage these children to look for a pattern as they investigate. Can they see which type of numbers have just one distinct prime factor?

Common misconceptions
Some children may be able to find the distinct prime factor but may not record correctly how many times it occurs. For example, the distinct prime factor of 16 is 2, occurring four times: 2 × 2 × 2 × 2. It may be incorrectly written as 2 × 2 × 2. Encourage children to recheck their answers, marking off each prime factor as it occurs.

Probing questions
● Is there a more efficient way to write 2 × 2 × 2? (2^3)
● Are there any particular types of number that have only one distinct prime factor? (Prime numbers, squares and cubes of prime numbers.)

Next steps
Support: Revisit prime factors and using factors to find the product of two-digit by two-digit calculations, to ensure children are confident with the requirements of this unit. Refer back to Year 6 Block B Unit 2.
Extension: Introduce 'powers' and give opportunities for children to find the answer to calculations such as 5 to the power 4. Refer also to the Year 6 extension or Year 7 material if appropriate.

Activity ⑥

Prior learning
Children understand the terms test of divisibility, approximate and inverse operation. They can round integers to the nearest 10, 100 or 1000, and decimals to the nearest whole number.

Framework objective
Use approximations, tests of divisibility and inverse operations to estimate and check results

Vocabulary
integer, decimal, round, estimate, approximate, inverse, divisibility, operation

Resources
Worksheet: Is it correct?

⑥ Is it correct?

Give out the worksheet 'Is it correct?'. The children are required to check calculations and statements using inverse operations, tests of divisibility and approximations.

Teacher support
Less confident learners: These children may need support with choosing the correct method to find the answer to the calculation/problem. If necessary, remind them of the rules for tests of divisibility.
More confident learners: These children should decide for themselves which is the most appropriate method to solve the question.

Common misconceptions
When using inverse operations to check calculations in a number sentence, children do not calculate in the correct order. For instance, for 'I think of a number, double it, then add 5. My answer is 69,' children may double 69, or may add 5 to 69 then halve.
Remind children to start at the end of the question, moving their finger back over the sentence and making jottings as they work out each section.

Probing questions
● Explain why statement x cannot be correct.
● Explain how you knew the answer to x.
● What would be the best method to use to check statement x?

Next steps
Support: Reinforce tests of divisibility, especially for the 6-times, 8-times and 9-times tables. Refer back to Year 6 Block B Unit 2.
Extension: Provide more opportunities for children to use the inverse operation to solve problems, especially word problems. Refer also to the Year 6 extension or Year 7 material if appropriate.

Activity ⑦

BLOCK B

| **Prior learning** Children are competent at using a calculator and know how to clear the memory should it be activated. | **Framework objective** Use a calculator to solve problems involving multi-step calculations |

Vocabulary
problem, solution, calculate, reasoning, method, inverse, operation, product

Resources
Display page: Know your calculator
Resource sheet: Self-assessment
Classroom resources: calculators

⑦ Know your calculator

Reveal the display page 'Know your calculator' and go through the questions with the children. Ask them to interpret the displays in the context of a calculator screen. They are also required to solve one-step and two-step calculations and word problems. Invite the children to devise their own problems, explaining when they would use a calculator and when they would use mental methods. Say, for example: *Make up a word problem to match these number sentences:*

● 4.8 ÷ 0.6
● 9 × 0.3

Decide whether to use the self-assessment sheet for the children to record their achievements and what they need to do next.

Teacher support
Less confident learners: Encourage these children to check their calculator after each problem is solved, as information is often left inadvertently in the memory. Remind them not to rush when entering information, and to press keys carefully, as information is often wrongly entered in these situations.
More confident learners: Encourage these children to consider carefully when they need to use a calculator. Get them to question whether it is sometimes more efficient to calculate mentally.

Common misconceptions
Some children are not secure in reading the display on a calculator and will find questions 1 and 2 challenging.
Ask these children to enter the display into their own calculator, thinking about place value as they do so. If necessary, a ready prepared place value heading chart may help some children; as they write down the display under each heading, they should recognise the absence of a zero in the calculator version of the answer.

Probing questions
● In what order did you have to work out this calculation?
● What was your estimation for this problem that helped you find the answer?
● Why does 0.3 on a calculator, in the context of money, mean 30p?

Next steps
Support: Provide more opportunities for calculator work, especially multi-step problems. Refer back to Year 6 Block B Unit 2.
Extension: Extend children's use of the full range of keys on their calculators (for example, memory button and the square root key) if they are not yet competent with them. Refer also to the Year 6 extension or Year 7 material if appropriate.

SCHOLASTIC

Activity ⑧

Prior learning
Children know the terms parallel, perpendicular, face, edge, vertex, prism and plane.

Framework objective
Describe, identify and visualise parallel and perpendicular edges or faces; use these properties to classify 2D shapes and 3D solids

Vocabulary
parallel, perpendicular, prism; names of 3D solids (cube, cuboid, sphere, cylinder, cone, triangular prism, square-/triangular-based pyramid)

Resources
Interactive activity: Shape sorter
Worksheet: Shape sorting
Classroom resources: set of solid shapes (cube, cuboid, sphere, cylinder, cone, triangular prism, square-based and triangular-based pyramids), isometric dotty paper, Multi-link

⑧ Shape sorting

Display the interactive activity 'Shape sorter'. Children are asked to sort shapes into a Carroll diagram according to their properties. In addition, on the accompanying worksheet 'Shape sorting' children have to create their own Venn diagrams and answer questions about properties of 3D solids.

Teacher support
Less confident learners: Some children may find it difficult to visualise some of the 3D shapes, so they will need to have the appropriate solids available to refer to.
More confident learners: These children will probably not find it necessary to tackle the interactive activity. Move them straight on to the worksheet.

Common misconceptions
Children forget to include the faces/edges/vertices that they cannot directly see (for example, those on the base if the solid is on the table).
Remind the children to visualise the shape all the way round, or, if using actual solids, pick up and count by touching each vertex/edge.

Probing questions
● Where should I put this shape in this Venn diagram?
● What properties of this shape prevent it from being placed in this section of the Carroll diagram?
● What can you tell me about the vertices/edges/faces of a cube and a cuboid?
● What do you notice about the numbers of faces and vertices in a polyhedron compared to the number of edges? (Faces + vertices = edges + 2)

Next steps
Support: Develop children's competence in knowing the vertices/faces/edges of 3D shapes by visualisation alone. Refer back to Year 6 Block B Unit 2.
Extension: Develop children's ability to visualise 3D solids from 2D shapes. For example, you could ask them to draw solids on isometric dotty paper and then build them with Multi-link. Refer also to the Year 6 extension or Year 7 material if appropriate.

BLOCK B

Activity ⑨

Prior learning Children can measure accurately to within 2mm when using a ruler. They can use a protractor to draw angles within 5° of accuracy.	**Framework objective** Make and draw shapes with increasing accuracy and apply knowledge of their properties **Vocabulary** diameter, radius, circumference, pentagon, hexagon, concentric **Resources** **Resource sheet:** Self-assessment **Classroom resources:** compasses, protractors, rulers, string

⑨ Drawing circles

Carry out this activity in small groups, with a teaching assistant. Ask the children to draw the following shapes, assessing their use of the compasses and the protractor. Aspects to consider include: How accurate are the children's measuring skills? Can they use compasses with confidence? What reasoning skills do they draw upon when solving problems? Do they use correct vocabulary when describing shapes? Here are some suggested shapes/questions to ask:
- a circle with a radius of 6cm
- a circle containing a regular octagon which has its vertices on the circumference of the circle
- a set of circles, one inside the other, with radii of 4cm, 5cm, 6cm and 7cm
- investigate the relationship between the radius and the diameter of these shapes
- [using a previously drawn circle] Estimate how many times the diameter of this circle will fit into the circumference. How can you check?

Decide whether to use the self-assessment sheet for the children to record their achievements and what they need to do next.

Teacher support
Less confident learners: For the second example above, you may need to support children in order to establish a starting point that will enable them to draw the octagon. Explain how to draw two diameters that are perpendicular and which will give the vertices of a square. Encourage group discussion as to how this may be developed to form an octagon.
More confident learners: Challenge these children to draw other regular shapes inside a circle (for example, pentagons and hexagons).

Common misconceptions
Some children may need additional time to master the use of the compasses. Show these children how to hold the compasses so that they do not open or close during the drawing of the circle.

Probing questions
- How far must you open the compasses to draw a circle with a diameter of 14cm?
- What size is each of the angles in the octagon?
- Estimate the diameter of this plate/saucer/coin/counter.

Next steps
Support: Give extra practice at drawing circles and shapes within circles using the range of equipment as detailed above. Refer back to Year 6 Block B Unit 2.
Extension: Introduce pi and explain how to find the area of a circle (πr^2). Ask the children to draw a variety of circles and find their areas. Refer also to the Year 6 extension or Year 7 material if appropriate.

Units 1, 2 & 3 ◾ Periodic assessment

These activities can be used at any time during the teaching of this block to assess those children that you think have achieved the objective. A grid highlighting the related assessment focuses and expected learning outcomes for each activity can be found on the CD-ROM.

Place value

Framework objective
Use knowledge of place value and multiplication facts to 10 × 10 to derive related multiplication and division facts involving decimals (for example, 0.8 × 7, 4.8 ÷ 6)

Learning outcome
● I can use table facts to work out other facts with decimals.

Provide each child with the worksheet 'Place value' and ask them to complete it. In the first section of the sheet they are required to identify the incorrect statements in a list of number sentences. In the second section they are asked to calculate the answers to some problems involving decimals.

Identifying shapes

Framework objective
Describe, identify and visualise parallel and perpendicular edges or faces; use these properties to classify 2D shapes and 3D solids

Learning outcome
● I can identify 2D shapes according to their properties.

Provide the children with copies of the worksheet 'Identifying shapes'. In this assessment activity they are required to draw the shapes described by the properties given.

Drawing shapes

Framework objective
Make and draw shapes with increasing accuracy and apply knowledge of their properties

Learning outcome
● I can make and draw 2D shapes and 3D solids accurately.

Provide the children with the worksheet 'Drawing shapes'. They are required to complete shapes drawn in oblique angles on a grid, and then complete an activity relating to the net of a cube.

Name   Date

Place value

1. Just the facts

Look at the following number sentences. Mark with a tick (✓) those statements that are correct and with a cross (✗) those that are incorrect.

3.6 × 100 = 36 ☐

74 ÷ 10 = 7.4 ☐

0.8 × 7 = 5.6 ☐

5.4 ÷ 6 = 0.9 ☐

7.2 ÷ 1.2 = 0.6 ☐

In the box below, write the correct number sentences for the calculations that you have marked as incorrect.

2. Decimal problems

I have £4.90 to spend in a sweet shop. I want to buy some bags of sweets costing 70p.

a) How many bags can I buy? _____

b) Write this as a number sentence _____

A length of ribbon measuring 8.1 metres is cut into nine equal lengths.

c) How long is each length of ribbon? _____

d) Write this as a number sentence _____

How easy?

Red
Amber
Green

How do you think you have done?

_____

_____

Identifying shapes

Read each description carefully, identify the shape and then draw it.

1. A regular quadrilateral that has one set of parallel lines.	**2.** A quadrilateral that has two sets of parallel sides of equal length.
3. A quadrilateral that has two sets of parallel sides but no perpendicular sides.	**4.** A shape with three sets of parallel sides but no perpendicular sides.
5. A quadrilateral with one set of parallel sides and one set of perpendicular sides.	**6.** Describe these shapes using the terms perpendicular and parallel. 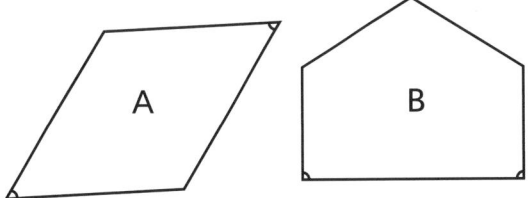 A _____ _____ B _____ _____

BLOCK B

Drawing shapes

1. Look at the incomplete shapes in the grid below.

a) Draw three more lines to complete the rectangle at (a).

b) Draw two more lines to complete the kite at (b).

c) Draw two more lines to complete the trapezium at (c).

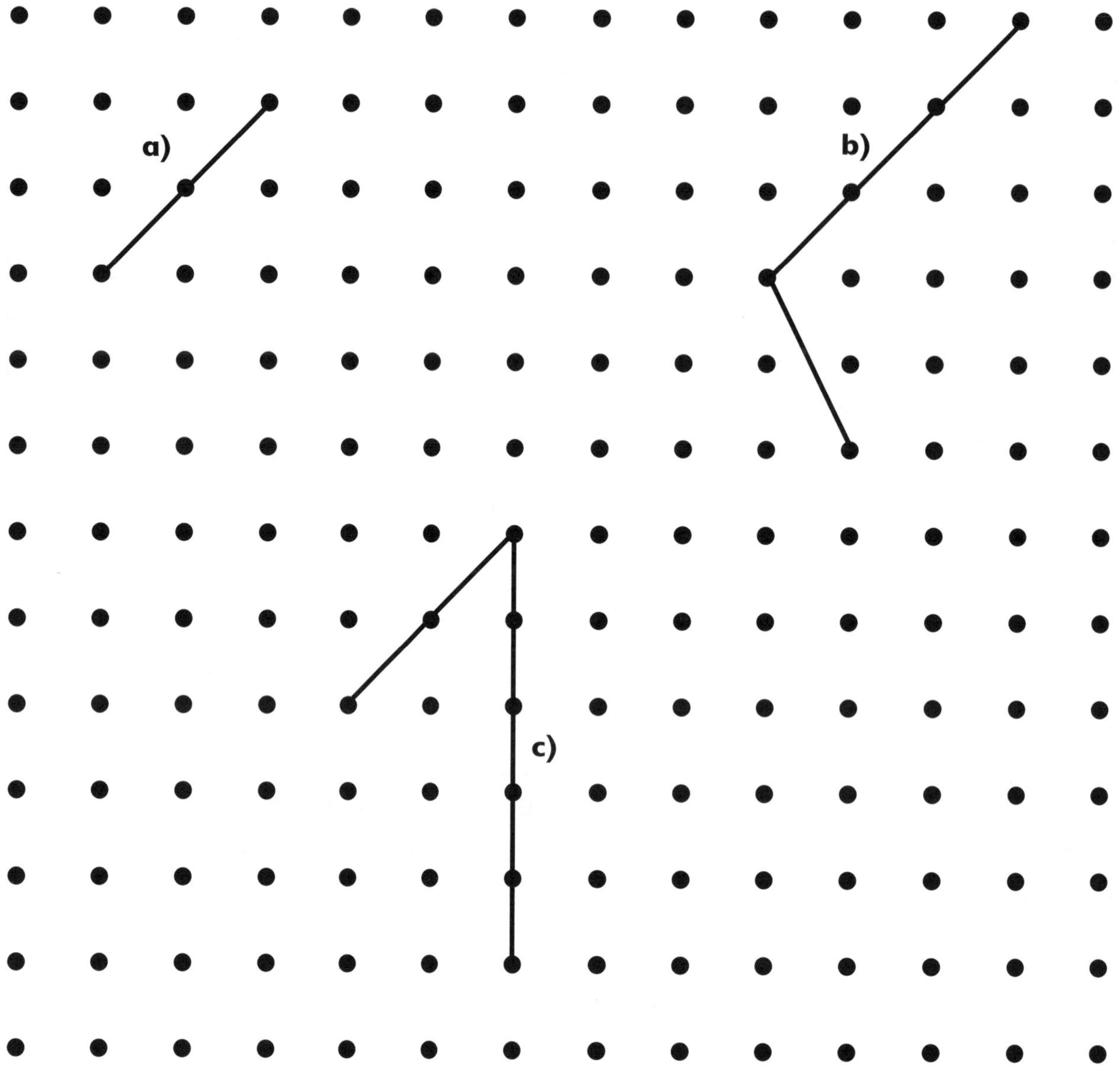

a)

b)

c)

2. Here is a drawing of a cube which has a pattern on three of its faces. Look at the net of the cube. Work out where the design will be and draw it on the net. One face has been done for you.

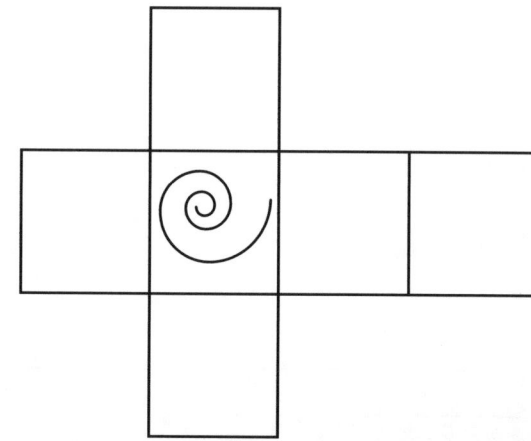

BLOCK C
Handling data and measures

Expected prior learning
Check that children can already:
- construct frequency tables, pictograms, bar charts and line graphs to represent the frequencies of events and changes over time
- collect, select and organise data to answer questions; draw conclusions and identify further questions to ask
- use ICT to collect, analyse, present and interpret information
- find and interpret the mode of a set of data
- describe the occurrence of familiar events using the language of chance or likelihood.

Objectives overview
The text in this diagram identifies the focus of mathematics learning within the block.

Key aspects of learning
- Enquiry
- Information processing
- Evaluation
- Communication

Collecting, processing, presenting and interpreting data to solve problems

Constructing frequency tables, bar charts for grouped discrete data and line graphs

Interpreting pie charts

Finding the mode, range, median and mean

Describing and interpreting results and solutions

Identifying further questions

BLOCK C: Handling data and measures

Estimating and measuring to required degree of accuracy

Metric units, conversions

Comparing readings from scales

Language of probability

Finding outcomes from data

Using ICT

Unit 1 ▪ Handling data and measures

Introduction
The formation and interpretation of different forms of graph provide the basis of this six-lesson block. The importance of graphs in other curriculum areas, especially science and geography, is emphasised. The unit explains the terms median, range, mode and mean and allows children to use them in context. Towards the end of the unit there are opportunities to revise the use of metric units of measurement and to check on children's ability to read a variety of measuring scales.

BLOCK C

Framework objectives	Assessment focuses		Success criteria for Year 6	Learning outcomes
	Level 5	Level 4		
① Silver challenge				
Suggest, plan and develop lines of enquiry; collect, organise and represent information, interpret results and review methods; identify and answer related questions	● ask questions, plan how to answer them and collect the data required	● collect discrete data, e.g. ● given a problem, suggest possible answers and data to collect ● test a hypothesis about the frequency of an event by collecting data ● group data, where appropriate, in equal class intervals, e.g. ● decide on a suitable class interval when collecting or representing data about pupils' hours per week spent watching TV	● can decide what information is needed to pursue any enquiry ● is able to collect information needed ● can organise, display and analyse information collected	I can suggest a line of enquiry and plan how to investigate it.
② Data handling				
Solve problems by collecting, selecting, processing, presenting and interpreting data, using ICT where appropriate; draw conclusions and identify further questions to ask	● interpret graphs and diagrams, including pie charts, and draw conclusions, e.g. ● complete a two-way table, given some of the data ● interpret bar graphs with grouped data ● interpret and compare pie charts where it is not necessary to measure angles ● read between labelled divisions on a scale ● recognise the difference between discrete and continuous data ● recognise when information is presented in a misleading way, e.g. compare two pie charts where the same sizes are different ● when drawing conclusions, identify further questions to ask	● interpret frequency diagrams and simple line graphs ● interpret simple pie charts ● interpret the scale on bar graphs and line graphs, reading between the labelled divisions, e.g. reading 17 on a scale labelled in fives ● interpret the total amount of data represented ● compare data sets and respond to questions, e.g. 'How does our data about favourite TV programmes compare to the data from Year 3 children?'	● recognises the common types of chart and graph used to show information ● can analyse and interpret information provided on charts and graphs	I can answer questions about the data I have represented.

78 100 MATHS ASSESSMENT LESSONS · YEAR 6

▪SCHOLASTIC

Unit 1 ▪ Handling data and measures

Framework objectives	Assessment focuses		Success criteria for Year 6	Learning outcomes
	Level 5	Level 4		
③ Maths test				
Construct and interpret frequency tables, bar charts with grouped discrete data, and line graphs; interpret pie charts	• create and interpret line graphs where the intermediate values have meaning, e.g. ○ draw and use a conversion graph for pounds and euro	• represent collected data in frequency diagrams • construct simple line graphs • continue to use Venn and Carroll diagrams to record their sorting and classifying of information	• selects graph/chart most appropriate to represent data • can decide on scale needed for graph • fully labels charts and graphs, especially axes • can make up questions when analysing graphs and charts	*I can represent data in different ways and understand its meaning.*
④ In training				
Describe and interpret results and solutions to problems using the mode, range, median and mean	• compare two simple distributions, using the range and one of mode, median or mean (mean and median are drawn from the Key Stage 3 Programme of Study), e.g. ○ describe and compare two sets of football results by using the range and mode	• understand and use the mode and range to describe sets of data, e.g. ○ use mode and range to describe data relating to shoe sizes in their class and begin to compare their data with data from another class	• understands the meanings of the words range, mode, median and mean • understands that mode, median and mean are all types of average • can find the range, mode, median and mean of sets of data • can solve problems using range and mean	*I can work out different types of average.*
⑤ All change				
Select and use standard metric units of measure and convert between units using decimals to two places	• solve problems involving the conversion of units, e.g. ○ solve problems such as 1.5kg ÷ 30g ○ work out approximately how many kilometres are equivalent to 20 miles	• choose and use appropriate units and instruments	• can convert one unit of measure to another using decimal numbers where appropriate • can use these conversions to assist with problem solving tasks	*I can convert from one unit of measure to another.*
⑥ Liquid measures				
Read and interpret scales on a range of measuring instruments, recognising that the measurement made is approximate and recording results to a required degree of accuracy; compare readings on different scales	• read and interpret scales on a range of measuring instruments, explaining what each labelled division represents	• interpret, with appropriate accuracy, numbers on a range of measuring instruments, e.g. ○ measure a length using millimetres, to within 2mm	• can read scales on a variety of measuring instruments • is able to explain what each labelled division represents on a scale • can compare readings on different scales • can represent the same quantity on different scales	*I can read scales and give my answers as accurately as the question asks.*

BLOCK C

Activity ①

BLOCK C

| **Prior learning** Children can suggest a possible line of enquiry and plan how they would investigate it. | **Framework objective** Suggest, plan and develop lines of enquiry; collect, organise and represent information, interpret results and review methods; identify and answer related questions |

Framework objective
Suggest, plan and develop lines of enquiry; collect, organise and represent information, interpret results and review methods; identify and answer related questions

Vocabulary
problem, solution, calculate, calculation, method, explain, reasoning, reason, predict, pattern, relationship, classify, represent, analyse, interpret

Resources
Resource sheet: Self-assessment
Classroom resources: clipboards, notepaper, pencils

① Silver challenge

This is largely an oral activity, with children working in groups of two or three. Present them with the following statement: *Davina says that the majority of cars seen on the roads today seem to be silver coloured.* Ask the children to discuss this and then make notes on how they would set out to discover whether this statement was true or false. What information would they need to pursue this enquiry? How would they collect, organise, display and analyse the information? Decide whether to use the self-assessment sheet for the children to record their achievements and what they need to do next.

Teacher support
Less confident learners: Make sure that the children have organised their findings in a logical way. It may help to set items down under headings that have been provided for them.
More confident learners: Extend these children by asking them to write a list of subject areas on which they could base a worthwhile enquiry, perhaps using a computer to help them.

Common misconceptions
Children believe that one type of chart or graph (for example, block or column graphs) can be used for all situations.
Encourage these children to think about the range of charts and graphs available and to consider which would be the most suitable to show the type of data collected.

Probing questions
● What does the data tell you about the original statement that is the subject of the enquiry?
● What further information could be collected to pursue the enquiry questions more fully?

Next steps
Support: Revise the steps the children went through to carry out the enquiry. Compile a bullet-pointed list that they could use for further enquiries. Refer back to Year 5 Block C Unit 1.
Extension: Encourage the children to extend the enquiry as much as possible. Other relevant questions might include the following: *Why do manufacturers produce so many silver cars? Why are they popular with motorists?* Refer also to Year 6 Block C Units 2 and 3.

Activity ②

Prior learning
Children can recognise the common types of charts and graphs used to show information. They can answer questions about the data that is represented on a chart or graph.

Framework objective
Solve problems by collecting, selecting, processing, presenting and interpreting data, using ICT where appropriate; draw conclusions and identify further questions to ask

Vocabulary
data, information, survey, questionnaire, graph, chart, table, scale, interval, division, horizontal axis, vertical axis, axes, label, title, pictogram, bar chart, bar line graph, line graph, pie chart

Resources
Interactive activity (ITP): Data handling
Resource sheet: Self-assessment

② Data handling

The aim of this activity is to present pre-set data to children so that they can analyse and interpret the information it provides. Choose one of the pre-set data options on the ITP 'Data handling'. Encourage the children to explore the data by creating a bar chart, pie chart or line graph. Decide whether to use the self-assessment sheet for the children to record their achievements and what they need to do next.

Teacher support
Less confident learners: Encourage these children to read the bars using just the scale. Hide the key and reveal it only at the end of the activity.
More confident learners: View the data as a pie chart. Ask questions such as: *What general statements can be made about the data? Could the data be translated into fractions?*

Common misconceptions
Children become confused about how information is shown on different types of graph.
Ensure that the children are able to name and describe the different parts of graphs and to explain the intervals, ranges and distribution of data.

Probing questions
● What statements about the data can be made before reading any numbers?
● Looking at the data in the pie chart, is it possible to identify any equivalent fractions in the information?

Next steps
Support: Interpreting data from all kinds of graphs, tables and charts is an important prerequisite for children to be able to sort data into self-made charts and graphs. Refer back to Year 5 Block C Units 1 and 2.
Extension: Challenge the children to think of other ways in which the information shown on these graphs and charts might be shown. Refer also to Year 6 Block C Units 2 and 3.

BLOCK C

Activity ③

Prior learning Children can represent given data in different ways and understand the meaning of this data.	**Framework objective** Construct and interpret frequency tables, bar charts with grouped discrete data and line graphs; interpret pie charts **Vocabulary** data, information, survey, questionnaire, graph, chart, table, scale, interval, division, horizontal axis, vertical axis, axes, label, title, pictogram, bar chart, bar line graph, line graph, pie chart **Resources** **Display page:** Maths test **Worksheet:** Maths test **Classroom resources:** graph paper

③ Maths test

Before providing the children with copies of the worksheet 'Maths test' to complete, you could explain the activity on the whiteboard using the corresponding display page. The children need to complete the table of grouped data to show the scores of the maths test, then construct a bar graph to show the results and analyse and interpret what they have found out.

Teacher support

Less confident learners: Some children may need help and support with organising the data, especially when choosing the most suitable graph paper and deciding what scale to use.

More confident learners: Ask questions such as: *Were the results produced as you expected them to be? Would a maths test carried out in your own class produce similar results?*

Common misconceptions

Children believe the result shown on the graph speaks for itself and does not require such detail as labelled axes, headings or scale details.
Give these children experience of trying to interpret badly labelled graphs so that they begin to realise the importance of such features.

Probing questions

● Was a bar graph the best choice to show this particular type of data? What reasons can you give for your choice?
● How did you decide what information to show on each of the axes?
● How did you decide what scale to use?

Next steps

Support: Provide help when children are analysing the finished graph at the end of the activity. What conclusions can be drawn? Refer back to Year 5 Block C Units 1 and 2.

Extension: Ask children to think of other situations in which a graph of this kind showing grouped data might be used. Suggest that they collect data and produce their own graph. Refer also to Year 6 Block C Units 2 and 3.

BLOCK C

Activity

Prior learning
Children can work out different types of average, especially the mean.

Framework objective
Describe and interpret results and solutions using the mode, range, median and mean

Vocabulary
frequency, mode, maximum, minimum, value, range, mean, average, median, statistics

Resources
Resource sheet: Self-assessment
Classroom resources: calculators

④ In training

In this practical task children can work in pairs or individually. Calculators can be used if necessary. Tell the children that Ashad is in training for a 100m running event. Write on the board his times for ten training runs (all times are in seconds): 13.4; 13.0; 13.9; 13.3; 13.7; 13.5; 14.0; 14.4; 13.8; 14.0. Ask the children the following questions:
● What is the range of the ten times shown?
● What is Ashad's mean (average) time?
When the children have completed this activity, decide whether to use the self-assessment sheet so that they can record their achievements and what they need to do next.

Teacher support
Less confident learners: If children are using calculators, make sure that the correct decimal numbers are input and that they are added carefully.
More confident learners: Challenge these children to make a close estimate of the mean before carrying out the calculations.

Common misconceptions
When children use real data they expect the mean to be one of the numbers involved rather than a number not included in the data set.
Show the children plenty of examples where this is obviously not the case. For example, the mean (average) mass of five bags of sand weighing 200g, 250g, 300g, 250g and 400g is 280g.

Probing questions
● Is the result of the task as you expected or did it show any surprises?
● In real-life situations, when would it help to be able to work out the mean (average) of a set of data?

Next steps
Support: Give children plenty of examples so that they are familiar with the difference between the mean and the range in a given set of numbers. Refer back to Year 5 Block C Unit 3.
Extension: Challenge the children to find a missing number/quantity when the other values and the mean are given. Refer also to Year 6 Block C Units 2 and 3.

BLOCK C

Activity ⑤

BLOCK C

Prior learning Children can convert from one unit of measure to another.	**Framework objective** Select and use standard metric units of measure and convert between units using decimals to two places (for example, change 2.75 litres to 2750ml or vice versa)

Vocabulary
estimate, measure, convert, gram (g), kilogram (kg), tonne (t), litre (l), centilitre (cl), millilitre (ml), millimetre (mm), centimetre (cm), metre (m), kilometre (km)

Resources
Interactive activity: All change

⑤ All change

Ask the children to perform a matching task using the interactive activity 'All change'. Two vertical lists of measures are given, written in different units. The children have to click and drag an arrow to join each item from the first set to the matching item in the second set.

Teacher support
Less confident learners: Make sure that the children's knowledge of decimal notation is sound before working on the conversion of metric units.
More confident learners: Encourage these children to write the same measurements in more than two different ways, if possible.

Common misconceptions
Children forget the importance of using the zero as a place holder.
Give children lots of practice at writing the conversions. For example, 10g should be written as 0.010kg; 3ml should be written as 0.003l.

Probing questions
● In a metric measurement written in decimal form, can you give the correct value of each digit?
● Which conversion do you find more difficult: larger units into small units or vice versa? Explain why.

Next steps
Support: Focus on making sure that the children appreciate the relationships within families of different units for length, mass and capacity. Refer back to Year 5 Block C Unit 3.
Extension: Ask children to work on conversions using less familiar units (for example, converting kilograms into tonnes and centilitres into litres). Refer also to Year 6 Block C Units 2 and 3.

Activity ⑥

Prior learning
Children can read scales and give answers accurately as the question asks.

Framework objective
Read and interpret scales on a range of measuring instruments, recognising that the measurement made is approximate and recording results to a required degree of accuracy; compare readings on different scales, for example when using different instruments

Vocabulary
estimate, measure, convert, scale, interval, gradation, millimetre (mm), centimetre (cm), metre (m), kilometre (km), gram (g), kilogram (kg), tonne (t), millilitre (ml), centilitre (cl), litre (l)

Resources
Worksheet: Liquid measures
Classroom resources: collection of measuring instruments such as: rulers, tapes, trundle wheels (length); clear containers and measuring cylinders (capacity); measuring scales, weights (mass)

⑥ Liquid measures

Provide the children with copies of the worksheet 'Liquid measures'. They are asked to read off levels on several measuring containers and also explain their reasoning.

Teacher support
Less confident learners: Display a selection of measuring cylinders and jugs prominently in the classroom so that the children become used to recognising different scales.
More confident learners: Encourage these children to work in situations where more complicated measuring scales are used (for example, millilitre intervals in 20s and 25s instead of 10s and 50s).

Common misconceptions
Children tend to count lines instead of spaces when working out what smaller interval markers represent on measuring scales.
Give these children plenty of opportunities to work with measuring scales where all intervals are clearly marked before asking them to work out intermediate divisions.

Probing questions
● Which divisions would help to provide more accurate results if you could add them to scales that you have used?
● Would it be practical to have a system where a common scale could be used for all measuring containers? What would be the advantages and the disadvantages?

Next steps
Support: Set up as many reinforcement tasks as possible involving estimating and reading scales, and scales using various containers filled with water. Refer back to Year 5 Block C Unit 3.
Extension: Challenge the children, working in pairs, to set up practical tasks and to make up their own scale-reading questions for a partner to solve. Refer also to Year 6 Block C Units 2 and 3.

Unit 2 ▪ Handling data and measures

Introduction

The using and applying mathematics activities that start this unit deal with the construction and interpretation of different forms of graphs, especially pie charts and line graphs. There is also revision of key data-handling terms such as range, mode, median and mean. Tasks explore the meaning of the words probability, likelihood and chance in practical situations. Working with metric units is revisited, as is reading and interpreting scales on measuring instruments.

BLOCK C

Framework objectives	Assessment focuses		Success criteria for Year 6	Learning outcomes
	Level 5	**Level 4**		

① Winning teams

Framework objectives	Level 5	Level 4	Success criteria for Year 6	Learning outcomes
Solve problems by collecting, selecting, processing, presenting and interpreting data, using ICT where appropriate; draw conclusions and identify further questions to ask	● interpret graphs and diagrams, including pie charts, and draw conclusions, e.g. ● complete a two-way table, given some of the data ● interpret bar graphs with grouped data ● interpret and compare pie charts where it is not necessary to measure angles ● read between labelled divisions on a scale ● recognise the difference between discrete and continuous data ● recognise when information is presented in a misleading way, e.g. compare two pie charts where the same sizes are different ● when drawing conclusions, identify further questions to ask	● interpret frequency diagrams and simple line graphs, e.g. ● interpret simple pie charts ● interpret the scale on bar graphs and line graphs, reading between the labelled divisions, e.g. reading 17 on a scale labelled in fives ● interpret the total amount of data represented ● compare data sets and respond to questions, e.g. 'How does our data about favourite TV programmes compare to the data from Year 3 children?'	● knows how to read and interpret a pie chart ● knows how to compare information shown on two or more pie charts ● can construct a pie chart given information	*I can use data to solve problems.*

② Warming up

Framework objectives	Level 5	Level 4	Success criteria for Year 6	Learning outcomes
Construct and interpret frequency tables, bar charts with grouped discrete data, and line graphs; interpret pie charts	● create and interpret line graphs where the intermediate values have meaning, e.g. ● draw and use a conversion graph for pounds and euro	● represent collected data in frequency diagrams, e.g. ● suggest an appropriate frequency diagram to represent particular data ● construct simple line graphs, e.g. ● decide upon an appropriate scale for a graph, e.g. labelled divisions representing 2, 5, 10, 100 ● continue to use Venn and Carroll diagrams to record their sorting and classifying of information	● can represent data in different ways and understand its meaning ● can interpret line graphs with simple *x* and *y* axes provided ● can decide on an appropriate scale to be used on a line graph ● is able to predict how a line graph might develop if continued	*I can represent data in different ways and understand their meaning.*

Unit 2 ◻ Handling data and measures

Framework objectives	Assessment focuses		Success criteria for Year 6	Learning outcomes
	Level 5	**Level 4**		
③ Dice throw				
Describe and interpret results and solutions to problems using the mode, range, median and mean	• compare two simple distributions, using the range and one of mode, median or mean (mean and median are drawn from the Key Stage 3 Programme of Study), e.g. ◦ describe and compare two sets of football results, by using the range and mode	• understand and use the mode and range to describe sets of data, e.g. ◦ use mode and range to describe data relating to shoe sizes in their class and begin to compare their data with data from another class	• can understand and define range, mode, median and mean • can find the mode, median and mean of a set of data • is able to explain how mode, median and mean problems are solved	*I can solve problems using mode, range, median and mean.*
④ In a spin				
Describe and predict outcomes from data using the language of chance or likelihood	• in probability, select methods based on equally likely outcomes and experimental evidence, as appropriate, e.g. ◦ decide whether a probability can be calculated or whether it can only be estimated from the results of an experiment • understand that different outcomes may result from repeating an experiment • understand and use the probability scale from 0 to 1 (from the Key Stage 3 Programme of Study) • use methods based on equally likely outcomes and experimental evidence, as appropriate, to find and justify probabilities, and approximations to these (from the Key Stage 3 Programme of Study) • interpret graphs and diagrams, including pie charts, and draw conclusions, e.g. ◦ describe and predict outcomes from data using the language of chance or likelihood	• collect discrete data, e.g. ◦ test a hypothesis about the frequency of an event by collecting data, e.g. collect dice scores to test ideas about how many scores of 6 will occur during 50 throws of a dice • interpret frequency diagrams and simple line graphs, e.g. ◦ in the context of data relating to everyday situations, understand the language of probability such as 'more likely', 'equally likely', 'fair', 'unfair', 'certain'	• understands the term probability and associated vocabulary such as likely, unlikely, impossible and even chance • uses and understands a probability scale based on 0-1 • can use a spinner in carrying out probability experiments • can compare the results on two spinners during probability experiments	*I can use data to work out problems about chance.*
⑤ Measuring jug				
Select and use standard metric units of measure and convert between units using decimals to two places (for example, change 2.75 litres to 2750ml, or vice versa)	• solve problems involving the conversion of units, e.g. ◦ solve problems such as 1.5kg ÷ 30g • make sensible estimates of a range of measures in relation to everyday situations	• choose and use appropriate units and instruments • interpret, with appropriate accuracy, numbers on a range of measuring instruments	• is able to convert one unit of measure to another using decimal numbers where appropriate • uses conversions to assist with problem-solving tasks • can follow a recipe where amounts have to be measured out	*I can convert measures between units including decimals.*

Unit 2 ◻ Handling data and measures

Framework objectives	Assessment focuses		Success criteria for Year 6	Learning outcomes
	Level 5	Level 4		
6 Level up				
Read and interpret scales on a range of measuring instruments, recognising that the measurement made is approximate and recording results to a required degree of accuracy; compare readings on different scales, for example when using different instruments	● read and interpret scales on a range of measuring instruments, explaining what each labelled division represents	● interpret, with appropriate accuracy, numbers on a range of measuring instruments, e.g. ● measure a length using millimetres, to within 2mm	● can read scales on a variety of measuring instruments ● can explain what each labelled division on a scale represents ● can compare readings on different scales ● can write metric measures in several different ways including the use of decimal numbers	*I can read and answer questions about scales and write down my answer as accurately as the question requires.* *I can compare readings from different scales.*
7 Make thirty				
Use a calculator to solve problems involving multi-step calculations	● use a calculator where appropriate to calculate fractions/percentages of quantities/measurements, e.g. ● find fractions of quantities such as $3/8$ of 980 ● find percentages such as 15% of 360g	● use inverse operations, e.g. ● use a calculator and inverse operations to find missing numbers, including decimals ● solve problems with or without a calculator	● can decide which calculations need the help of a calculator ● understands and uses the number and function keys on a calculator ● can read and interpret answers provided by a calculator ● can explain to others how they used a calculator to solve a problem	*I can use a calculator to solve problems involving more than one step.*

■SCHOLASTIC

Activity ①

Prior learning
Children can use data to solve problems.

Framework objective
Solve problems by collecting, selecting, processing, presenting and interpreting data, using ICT where appropriate; draw conclusions and identify further questions to ask

Vocabulary
data, information, survey, questionnaire, graph, chart, table, scale, interval, division, horizontal axis, vertical axis, axes, label, title, pictogram, bar chart, bar line graph, line graph, pie chart

Resources
Worksheet: Winning teams

① Winning teams

Hand out copies of the worksheet 'Winning teams'. This shows two pie charts recording the results of hockey matches played by two school teams. The children are required to compare the results shown on the two pie charts related to the same topic but based on different totals.

Teacher support
Less confident learners: Remind these children that on pie charts the whole of the circle has to be used and that no blank spaces are left.
More confident learners: Ask these children to collect and interpret examples of pie charts from written media. They are a popular way of showing information in magazines and newspapers.

Common misconceptions
Children assume that because half of each pie chart is labelled 'won' in this example, both schools must have won the same number of games.
Emphasise that the size of the fractions or percentages shown on the pie charts are based on the total numbers of games played by each school which here are different.

Probing questions
● How helpful is this type of graph in answering the questions that have been asked?
● Were the results as you expected or were there any surprises?

Next steps
Support: Ask children to make their own simple pie charts. Provide support with rounding off numbers, calculating sectors and drawing lines in the correct places. Refer back to Year 6 Block C Unit 1.
Extension: Challenge children to make their own pie charts from blank circles, calculating their own angles and marking them using a 360° protractor.
Refer also to Year 6 Block C Unit 3.

Activity ②

BLOCK C

Prior learning Children can represent data in different ways and understand its meaning.	**Framework objective** Construct and interpret frequency tables, bar charts and grouped discrete data and line graphs; interpret pie charts
	Vocabulary data, information, survey, questionnaire, graph, table, scale, interval, division, horizontal axis, vertical axis, axes, label, title, pictogram, bar chart, bar line graph, line graph, pie chart
	Resources **Interactive activity:** Warming up

② Warming up

In this activity, the children will be using the interactive activity 'Warming up'. In the blank table, type the data about temperature readings (given below). Click on 'line graph' to create the graph. As a class, decide on a title for the graph as well as labels for each axis. Ask the children to explain why they think the temperature rises and falls at certain times. *What other facts can you state about the information shown? How might the graph look if it was continued to 8pm?* Extra rows can be added to the data table in order to continue the graph.

Temperatures taken outside the school building, in the shade, on the hour every hour:

8am	8°C	9am	9°C
10am	10°C	11am	12°C
12noon	16°C	1pm	16°C
2pm	14°C	3pm	12°C

Teacher support
Less confident learners: Provide support to ensure that children read the information on the graph correctly and that they are able to label it correctly.
More confident learners: Ask these children to provide sound reasoning before they mark on the graph the predicted temperatures between 3pm and 8pm.

Common misconceptions
Children believe the lines joining the points show the exact temperature at the times between the hourly readings.
Point out that the lines are drawn to show the trend in the rise and fall of the temperature and do not necessarily show temperatures at the points between hourly readings.

Probing questions
● Is there another type of line graph that could be used to show this type of information?
● What evidence could be used to help to make the predictions of what the temperature would be between 3pm and 8pm?

Next steps
Support: Provide plenty of examples of line graphs so that children get used to plotting positions on the grid and reading off the information shown. Refer back to Year 6 Block C Unit 1.
Extension: Encourage children to make a similar graph using temperatures that they have collected themselves. *How does it compare with the graph data given?* Refer also to Year 6 Block C Unit 3.

Activity ③

Prior learning Children can solve problems using mode, range, median and mean.	**Framework objective** Describe and interpret results and solutions to problems using mode, range, median and mean **Vocabulary** frequency, mode, maximum, minimum, value, range, mean, average, median, statistics **Resources** **Resource sheet:** Self-assessment

③ Dice throw

This task can be carried out as an oral/practical activity. The children, individually or in pairs, can either work on their own or with the teacher/ teaching assistant. Tell them that Matthew throws a 1–6 dice 20 times and records these results (given below). Write the results on the board. Ask the children to find the mode, median and mean of this set of data and to explain how they determined the answers. (Mode 5; median 3.5; mean 3.15.)

4, 2, 5, 4, 5, 5, 2, 4, 3, 5, 3, 4, 3, 2, 2, 1, 6, 1, 1, 5

When the children have completed this activity, decide whether to use the self-assessment sheet so that they can record their achievements and next steps.

Teacher support
Less confident learners: Provide adult support to help these children calculate the mode, median and mean of the set of results.
More confident learners: Remind these children that some of the answers will produce decimal numbers but that calculations should be done without a calculator.

Common misconceptions
Children still get confused between the meanings of the different averages – mode, median and mean.
Try various methods to explain the meaning of the words to the children. For example, tell them that mode comes from the French 'à la mode' meaning fashionable (the most popular). Talk about Micky 'The Pig' Median who is always 'piggy in the middle'.

Probing questions
● Which of the operations to find the mode, median and mean of data do you find most difficult to carry out? Why do you think that is?
● In what practical situations would finding the mode, median and mean of a set of data prove useful?

Next steps
Support: Recap on the methods used for finding the mode and the mean – particularly the median when there are 'two' middle numbers. Refer back to Year 6 Block C Unit 1.
Extension: Encourage children to research and find real-life data for which to work out the mean, mode, median and range. Refer also to Year 6 Block C Unit 3.

BLOCK C

Activity ④

BLOCK C

Prior learning
Children can use data to work out problems about chance.

Framework objective
Describe and predict outcomes from data using the language of chance or likelihood

Vocabulary
fair, unfair, risk, doubt, likely, unlikely, equally likely, likelihood, certain, uncertain, probably, possibly, impossible, chance, good chance, poor chance, no chance, equal chance, even chance, outcome, biased, random

Resources
Display page: In a spin
Worksheet: In a spin
Classroom resources: card, hexagon template, paper fasteners to make spinners, rulers

④ In a spin

Reveal the display page 'In a spin' and go through the questions with the class. Then provide the children with copies of the corresponding worksheet and ask them to complete it individually. Have supplies of cardboard and paper fasteners available so that the children can make the spinners and test out their theories.

Teacher support
Less confident learners: Give these children plenty of opportunities to work on practical probability tasks involving limited outcomes and simple equipment such as dice, coins, playing cards and so on.
More confident learners: Challenge these children to devise other probability tasks using spinners similar to those used on the worksheet.

Common misconceptions
Children believe that some of the events discussed in probability activities are certain to happen.
Stress throughout that probability is not a measure of the absolute certainty of something happening, rather it provides a measure of the likelihood of an outcome.

Probing questions
● List three events that are possible. What about three that are certain?
● Place these (given) events on a probability line ranged from 0 (impossible) at one end to 1 (certain) at the other.

Next steps
Support: Help with methods of recording or provide printed record sheets when children are conducting probability experiments. Refer back to Year 5 Block C Unit 2.
Extension: Ask children to devise a simple experiment that could be used to collect data that would help towards answering a probability problem. For example: *What is the probability of a piece of toast landing butter side up if it is dropped on the floor?* Refer also to Year 6 Block C Unit 3.

Activity ⑤

Prior learning
Children can convert measures between units, including decimals.

Framework objective
Select and use standard metric units of measure and convert between units using decimals to two places (for example change 2.75 litres to 2750ml, or vice versa)

Vocabulary
estimate, measure, convert, gram (g), kilogram (kg), tonne (t), litre (l), millilitre (ml), centilitre (cl), millimetre (mm), centimetre (cm), metre (m), kilometre (km)

Resources
Interactive activity: Measuring jug

⑤ Measuring jug

Display the interactive activity 'Measuring jug'. Use the 'in' and 'out' taps to fill or empty the jug as required. Each time, ask the children to give the readings, first in millimetres and then in litres using decimals. For example, 3200ml would be 3.2 litres. The difference between two levels can also be found by filling and emptying the jug.

Teacher support
Less confident learners: In the early stages, ask these children to read the scale to the nearest 200ml mark.
More confident learners: These children should be able to give more accurate results and give measures in a third way (for example, 3200ml = 3.2 litres = 3 litres 200ml).

Common misconceptions
Children may try to hold a ruler beside a cylindrical container and try to read the capacity of its contents. They have not grasped that a measuring cylinder scale is measuring in three dimensions, not just height.
It might help if these children make their own measuring jug using a 50ml or 100ml container to obtain marked intervals.

Probing questions
● I have filled the container to 4400ml. What is that in litres?
● I have filled the container to 7.9 litres. What is that in millilitres?

Next steps
Support: Discuss with the children what kind of units they would use to measure certain amounts of liquid - for example, a glass of fruit juice (ml), Refer back to Year 5 Block C Unit 3.
a bottle of wine (cl) and a tank of petrol (l). Refer back to Year 6 Block C Unit 1.
Extension: Ask children to follow a simple recipe where accurate amounts of liquids have to be measured out (for example, making a jelly). Refer also to Year 6 Block C Unit 3.

Activity ⑥

<table>
<tr>
<td>

Prior learning
Children can read and answer questions about scales and write down answers as accurately as the question requires. They can compare readings from different scales.

</td>
<td>

Framework objective

Read and interpret scales on a range of measuring instruments, recognising that the measurement made is approximate and recording results to a required degree of accuracy; compare readings on different scales, for example when using different instruments

Vocabulary

estimate, measure, convert, scale, interval, gradation, millimetre (mm), centimetre (cm), metre (m), kilometre (km), gram (g), kilogram (kg), tonne (t), millilitre (ml), centilitre (cl), litre (l)

Resources
Worksheet: Level up
Classroom resources: spring balances (optional)

</td>
</tr>
</table>

⑥ Level up

The children should work independently on the worksheet 'Level up'. On this sheet they are shown four spring-balance weighing devices and have to mark on them the masses given. All the masses given are written as decimal fractions of a kilogram.

Teacher support

Less confident learners: Look at each of the spring-balance scales with the children so that they appreciate that they are all different and have different interval markings.
More confident learners: Talk about the heaviest masses that can be measured on each of the spring balances, and discuss what objects might be suitable for weighing on them.

Common misconceptions

Children assume that weighing devices are ready to record mass when an object is placed on them.
Make these children aware that scales need to be 'zeroed' before starting weighing and that weighing devices become less accurate or faulty through moving them about or misusing them.

Probing questions

● Which of the spring balances did you find easiest to mark with the mass? Why?
● Which of the spring balances did you find most difficult to mark with the mass? Why?

Next steps

Support: Emphasise that children should always make sure that they can read the scale of a measuring device first, before using it for any practical work. Refer back to Year 6 Block C Unit 1.
Extension: Challenge children to devise a practical experiment where they can find 'the best buy' by comparing different packages that have different masses of the same commodity (for example, different-sized cereal boxes). Refer also to Year 6 Block C Unit 3.

BLOCK C

Activity ⑦

Prior learning
Children can use a calculator to solve problems involving multi-step calculations.

Framework objective
Use a calculator to solve problems involving multi-step calculations

Vocabulary
problem, solution, calculate, calculation, operation, answer, method, strategy, explain, reason, calculator, function, key, display, enter, clear

Resources
Resource sheet: Self-assessment
Classroom resources: calculators

⑦ Make thirty

Provide each child with a calculator. Explain that they can only use the keys 3, 5, + and = on the calculator. Challenge them to find which of the numbers up to 30 they can make and to record their results on a piece of paper. (They should find that they can make all numbers greater than 3, except 4 and 7.) Decide whether to use the self-assessment sheet for the children to record their achievements and what they need to do next.

Teacher support
Less confident learners: Encourage these children to focus on making some of the easier numbers first (for example, 3 + 3 = 6 and 3 + 5 = 8). They can then use knowledge of these numbers to help them make the larger numbers.
More confident learners: Ask these children to investigate how far beyond 30 they can go still using the same four calculator keys. Is there a point when they have to stop?

Common misconceptions
Children believe that because it is a machine the calculator will always work properly and come up with the right answer.
Point out that it is the person operating the machine, not the calculator itself, that is the decision maker.

Probing questions
● Describe the keys you use, and the order you pressed them, for that calculation.
● Can you interpret what the display on the calculator shows? Explain how you know.

Next steps
Support: Encourage children to cut down on working-out time by first making sensible guesses about which numbers to enter into the calculator for a specific calculation. Refer back to Year 6 Block A Units 1, 2 and 3.
Extension: Children can repeat this activity using two different single-digit numbers and/or other operation keys. Refer also to Year 6 Block D Units 1, 2 and 3; Block E Units 1, 2 and 3.

BLOCK C

Unit 3 ▪ Handling data and measures

Introduction

Using and applying mathematical skills to solve practical problems dominates much of the work in this unit. Children are encouraged to make their own decisions throughout. There is an opportunity to revise the terms range, median, mode and mean, and a probability activity is also included. The use of measuring equipment is featured and calculator skills are developed in a practical context.

BLOCK C

Framework objectives	Assessment focuses		Success criteria for Year 6	Learning outcomes
	Level 5	Level 4		
① Wet weather				
Solve problems by collecting, selecting, processing, presenting and interpreting data, using ICT where appropriate; draw conclusions and identify further questions to ask	• interpret graphs and diagrams, including pie charts, and draw conclusions, e.g. ● complete a two-way table, given some of the data ● interpret bar graphs with grouped data ● interpret and compare pie charts where it is not necessary to measure angles ● read between labelled divisions on a scale ● recognise the difference between discrete and continuous data ● recognise when information is presented in a misleading way, e.g. compare two pie charts where the sample sizes are different ● when drawing conclusions, identify further questions to ask	• interpret frequency diagrams and simple line graphs, e.g. ● interpret simple pie charts ● interpret the scale on bar graphs and line graphs, reading between the labelled divisions, e.g. reading 17 on a scale labelled in fives ● interpret the total amount of data represented ● compare data sets and respond to questions, eg 'How does our data about favourite TV programmes compare to the data from Year 3 children?'	• is familiar with a range of different charts and graphs and their uses • reads and interprets a bar-line graph • can draw conclusions from a graph and identify further questions to be asked • uses the information shown on charts, graphs, etc to solve problems	*I can collect and present data in a variety of ways and use my results to solve problems.*
② Top speed				
Construct and interpret frequency tables, bar charts with grouped discrete data, and line graphs; interpret pie charts	• create and interpret line graphs where the intermediate values have meaning, e.g. ● draw and use a conversion graph for pounds and euro	• represent collected data in frequency diagrams, e.g. ● suggest an appropriate frequency diagram to represent particular data • construct simple line graphs, e.g. ● decide upon an appropriate scale for a graph, e.g. labelled divisions representing 2, 5, 10, 100 • continue to use Venn and Carroll diagrams to record their sorting and classifying of information	• can decide the best type of chart or graph to display given information • is able to interpret data that has been displayed • chooses a suitable scale when constructing a chart or graph	*I can represent data in a variety of ways and answer questions about the data, including interpreting pie charts.*

▪SCHOLASTIC

Unit 3 ▢ Handling data and measures

Framework objectives	Assessment focuses		Success criteria for Year 6	Learning outcomes
	Level 5	**Level 4**		
③ Blank cards				
Describe and interpret results and solutions to problems using the mode, range, median and mean	• compare two simple distributions, using the range and one of mode, median or mean (mean and median are drawn from the Key Stage 3 Programme of Study), e.g. ○ describe and compare two sets of football results, by using the range and mode	• understand and use the mode and range to describe sets of data, e.g. ○ use mode and range to describe data relating to shoe sizes in their class and begin to compare their data with data from another class	• understands and can define range, mode, median and mean • can find sets of data required when provided with range, mode, median and mean • can explain how problems were solved • can give examples of where range, mode, median and mean occur in everyday practical situations	*I can use the different averages to solve problems.*
④ Even chance				
Describe and predict outcomes from data using the language of chance or likelihood	• in probability, select methods based on equally likely outcomes and experimental evidence, as appropriate, e.g. ○ decide whether a probability can be calculated or whether it can only be estimated from the results of an experiment • understand that different outcomes may result from repeating an experiment • understand and use the probability scale from 0 to 1 • use methods based on equally likely outcomes and experimental evidence, as appropriate, to find and justify probabilities, and approximations to these (both from the Key Stage 3 Programme of Study) • interpret graphs and diagrams, including pie charts, and draw conclusions, e.g. ○ describe and predict outcomes from data using the language of chance or likelihood	• collect discrete data, e.g. ○ test a hypothesis about the frequency of an event by collecting data, eg collect dice scores to test ideas about how many scores of 6 will occur during 50 throws of a dice • interpret frequency diagrams and simple line graphs, e.g. ○ in the context of data relating to everyday situations, understand the language of probability such as 'more likely', 'equally likely', 'fair', 'unfair', 'certain'	• understands the term probability and associated vocabulary such as certain, impossible, unlikely, etc • uses and understands a probability scale based on 0–1 • can use a spinner to carry out probability experiments • can devise simple probability experiments • can apply probability events to real-life situations	*I can use the language of chance to solve problems.*
⑤ Convert the weight				
Select and use standard metric units of measure and convert between units using decimals to two places (e.g. change 2.75 litres to 2750ml, or vice versa)	• solve problems involving the conversion of units, e.g. ○ solve problems such as 1.5kg ÷ 30g ○ work out approximately how many kilometres are equivalent to 20 miles	• choose and use appropriate units and instruments	• can convert one unit of measure to another using decimal numbers • can convert metric measures into a common family to help calculations	*I can convert measures between units including decimals.*

100 MATHS ASSESSMENT LESSONS · YEAR 6 ▢ 97

Unit 3 ⬜ Handling data and measures

Framework objectives	Assessment focuses		Success criteria for Year 6	Learning outcomes
	Level 5	Level 4		
⑥ Flying arrows				
Read and interpret scales on a range of measuring instruments, recognising that the measurement made is approximate and recording results to a required degree of accuracy; compare readings on different scales, for example when using different instruments	• read and interpret scales on a range of measuring instruments, explaining what each labelled division represents	• interpret, with appropriate accuracy, numbers on a range of measuring instruments, eg • measure a length using millimetres, to within 2mm	• is able to read scales on a variety of measuring instruments • can explain what each labelled division represents on a scale • can compare readings on different scales • can record the same quantity on a range of different scales	*I can read and answer questions about scales and write down my answer as accurately as the question requires.* *I can compare readings from different scales.*
⑦ Conversion graph				
Use a calculator to solve problems involving multi-step calculations	• use a calculator where appropriate to calculate fractions/percentages of quantities/measurements, e.g. • find fractions of quantities such as $^3/_8$ of 980 • find percentages such as 15% of 360g	• use inverse operations, e.g. • use a calculator and inverse operations to find missing numbers, including decimals • solve problems with or without a calculator	• is able to decide when a calculator should be used to help calculations • can use a calculator to convert one form of currency into another • can explain to others how a calculator was used to solve a problem	*I can solve problems involving more than one step.*

BLOCK C

◾SCHOLASTIC

Activity ①

Prior learning
Children can collect and present data in a variety of forms and then use the results collected from data to solve problems.

Framework objective
Solve problems by collecting, selecting, processing, presenting and interpreting data, using ICT where appropriate; draw conclusions and identify further questions to ask

Vocabulary
data, information, survey, questionnaire, graph, chart, table, scale, interval, division, horizontal axis, vertical axis, axes, label, title, pictogram, bar chart, bar-line graph, line graph, pie chart

Resources
Worksheet: Wet weather

① Wet weather

Provide each child with a copy of the worksheet 'Wet weather', on which a bar-line graph shows the monthly rainfall in the Lake District during one year. The rain was collected and measured to the nearest centimetre. Ask the children to suggest at least four questions that they could ask about the data shown on the graph, and to supply answers to their questions.

Teacher support
Less confident learners: Make sure that these children read the labelled axes carefully. Help may be needed with interpreting the scale used.
More confident learners: Ask these children to suggest other topics that would be suitable for showing in the form of a bar-line graph like the one shown.

Common misconceptions
Children become confused in the switch over from block or column graphs to bar-line graphs, which show data using a single vertical line.
Emphasise that bar-line graphs are, in many ways, easier to read as they are only about checking height or length rather than having to count squares.

Probing questions
● Would a different scale have made it easier to read off the data more quickly? Suggest what scale could have been used.
● Why would it be inappropriate to join the tops of the sticks on the graph showing this kind of data?

Next steps
Support: When children are making their own bar-line graphs, use clearly marked squared paper to assist with the choice of scale. Refer back to Year 6 Block C Unit 1.
Extension: Discuss which organisations and individuals would find the data about rainfall in this region useful. Refer also to the Year 6 extension or Year 7 material if appropriate.

BLOCK C

Activity ②

BLOCK C

Prior learning
Children can represent data in a variety of ways and can answer questions about data.

Framework objective
Construct and interpret frequency tables, bar charts with grouped discrete data and line graphs; interpret pie charts

Resources
Display page: Top speed
Resource sheet: Self-assessment
Classroom resources: variety of squared paper and other materials for making graphs

② Top speed

The children should carry out this practical assessment task individually or in pairs. Show the display page 'Top speed' which gives the speeds of eight of the fastest land mammals, in short bursts. Challenge the children to find the best way of representing the data in the form of a graph of their choice. Also encourage them to write comments about what the graph shows. Once they have done this, decide whether to use the self-assessment sheet for the children to record their achievements and what they need to do next.

Teacher support
Less confident learners: Assist these children with the choice of scale and what information to represent on the horizontal and vertical axes of their graph.
More confident learners: Ask these children to find the approximate fastest speed for a human by researching the time taken by athletes at the Olympic Games. Compare the result with the other data.

Common misconceptions
Children assume that the x-axis should always detail the category while the y-axis should always show frequency or amount.
Encourage these children to reverse the roles of the axes and ensure that they see a range of ways of presenting different graphs and charts.

Probing questions
● What decisions did you have to make when choosing a suitable scale for the data to be shown in the graph?
● Was only one kind of graph suitable for the data or were there other possibilities that would also have worked?

Next steps
Support: Keep examples of different types of charts and graphs on display in the classroom so that children become familiar with how they are used. Refer back to Year 6 Block C Units 1 and 2.
Extension: Make sure that children are able to briefly describe the appearance and function of each of the main types of graph that they have come across in this and previous units. For example, a pie chart: this type of graph is based on the sectors of a circle. Refer also to the Year 6 extension or Year 7 material if appropriate.

Activity ③

Prior learning
Children can use the different forms of average to solve problems.

Framework objective
Describe and interpret results and solutions to problems using the mode, range, median and mean

Vocabulary
frequency, mode, maximum, minimum, value, range, mean, average, median, statistics

Resources
Resource sheet: Self-assessment
Classroom resources: felt-tipped pens, pieces of card (playing card size)

③ Blank cards

The children should carry out this practical/oral activity individually. There are four tasks:
● Give each child five cards and a felt-tipped pen. Ask them to write a number on each card so that the mode of the five numbers is 12.
● Give the children another five cards. Ask them to write five numbers so that the median of the numbers is 15.
● Give the children another five cards. Ask them to list five different numbers between 0 and 20. Ask them to find the range.
● Give out another three cards to each child. Ask them to write three numbers so that the mean of the numbers is 8.
Decide whether to use the self-assessment sheet for the children to record their achievements and what they need to do next.

Teacher support
Less confident learners: Remind the children that the mean, median and mode are all types of average – they summarise data in different ways.
More confident learners: Ask these children to investigate how the mean could be used for cricket scores to work out a batter's average score.

Common misconceptions
Children think there is only ever one mode and that if there are two middle numbers the median cannot be found.
Point out that there can sometimes be more than one mode and that when there are two middle numbers the median is halfway between them.

Probing questions
● Can you think of any real-life situations in which finding the different kinds of average in a set of data would be useful?
● Which of the three types of average do you think is the most useful to find out? Why?

Next steps
Support: Check the accuracy of calculations involved in finding averages, especially the mean (found by totalling then dividing by how many values there are). Refer back to Year 6 Block C Units 1 and 2.
Extension: Ask children to throw a dice 20 times and record the results. Then ask them to calculate the mean, median, range and mode of the numbers recorded. Refer also to the Year 6 extension or Year 7 material if appropriate.

BLOCK C

Activity ④

Prior learning
Children can use the language of chance to solve problems.

Framework objective
Describe and predict outcomes from data using the language of chance and likelihood

Vocabulary
fair, unfair, risk, doubt, likely, unlikely, equally unlikely, likelihood, certain, uncertain, probable, possible, impossible, chance, good chance, poor chance, no chance, equal chance, even chance, outcome, biased, random

Resources
Resource sheet: Self-assessment
Classroom resources: card, paper fasteners to make spinners

④ Even chance

Ask the children to make a spinner from a square of card. They should divide the square into eight equal parts. Each of the parts should be labelled with a number using only the digits 1, 2, 3 and 4. Set them this task: *Place the digits in the spaces on the square so that there is an even chance that the spinner will land on either 2 or 4. All numbers must be used at least once.* Decide whether to use the self-assessment sheet for the children to record their achievements and what they need to do next.

Teacher support
Less confident learners: Ensure that the four digits are used at least once on the square spinner and that no sections of the square are left blank.
More confident learners: Challenge these children to devise other probability problems using the same kind of square spinner and the four digits. They could make up different statements which could be proved to be true or false.

Common misconceptions
Children become confused and think even-chance solutions can only be connected to the use of even numbers.
Emphasise that 'even chance' is a term used for events that are just as likely to happen as they are not to happen, and can apply to any number.

Probing questions
● Tell me some situations in which other probability terms might be used. (For example, very unlikely, unlikely, likely and very likely.)
● In what kind of real-life situations would probability and likelihood have any real value?

Next steps
Support: Spend time discussing the meaning of probability terms so that children become fully conversant with them. Refer back to Year 6 Block C Units 1 and 2.
Extension: Challenge children to devise and demonstrate a probability task involving the use of a set of playing cards or some coloured balls placed in a bag. Refer also to the Year 6 extension or Year 7 material if appropriate.

Activity ⑤

Prior learning
Children can convert measures between units including decimals.

Framework objective
Select and use standard metric units of measure and convert between units using decimals to two places (for example, change 2.75 litres to 2750ml, or vice versa)

Vocabulary
estimate, measure, convert, gram (g), kilogram (kg), tonne (t), litre (l), millilitre (ml), centilitre (cl), millimetre (ml), centimetre (cm), metre (m), kilometre (km)

Resources
Interactive activity: Convert the weight
Classroom resources: individual whiteboards and pens

⑤ Convert the weight

Introduce the interactive activity 'Convert the weight'. In this activity, the children are asked to accurately read and convert kilograms to grams (and vice versa). Drag an item into the pan and ask the children, working in pairs, to write down the mass of the item on their whiteboards using decimals and the notation that is opposite to that used on the screen.

Teacher support
Less confident learners: Provide adult assistance to help these children to read the scales accurately.
More confident learners: Record the initial mass of the food items, then remove two items and record the new mass. What is the difference between the two masses?

Common misconceptions
Children experience difficulty adding and subtracting metric amounts when mixed units are given – for example, finding the total mass of parcels weighing 1.25kg, 400g and 0.60kg.
Encourage children to change units in the same family so they are all the same before carrying out the calculation. For example, in the example given, change to 1.25kg + 0.40kg + 0.60kg or 1250g + 400g + 600g.

Probing questions
● How could you use the mass of the bag of flour to help estimate the mass of the other products? What other food products would be useful guides?
● What is the total mass of these two items in grams and kilograms?

Next steps
Support: Spend time reinforcing the relationship between metric units (for example, 1000g = 1kg; 1000kg = 1 tonne). Refer back to Year 6 Block C Units 1 and 2.
Extension: Encourage children to make up their own simple problems in which metric measures have to be converted from one type of units to another to make calculations easier. Refer also to Year 6 Block D Units 1, 2 and 3.

Activity ⑥

Prior learning
Children can read and answer questions about scales. They can write down an answer as accurately as the question requires. They can compare readings from different scales.

Framework objective
Read and interpret scales on a range of measuring instruments, recognising that the measurement made is approximate and recording results to a required degree of accuracy; compare readings on different scales, for example when using different instruments

Vocabulary
estimate, measure, convert, scale, interval, division, gradation, millimetre (mm), centimetre (cm), metre (m), kilometre (km), gram (g), kilogram (kg), millilitre (ml), litre (l), centilitre (cl)

Resources
Worksheet: Flying arrows
Classroom resources: centimetre and metre rulers for reference

⑥ Flying arrows

Provide the children with copies of the worksheet 'Flying arrows' and ask them to complete it. On this sheet they are shown three measuring scales involving mass and must mark the same mass on all three scales, despite the fact that the scales being used are all different.

Teacher support
Less confident learners: Provide plenty of opportunities for these children to examine and work with measuring instruments that have different scales. Encourage them to annotate the scales to help them read off values.
More confident learners: Ask these children to use arrows to show other examples of masses that could be measured on the same three scales.

Common misconceptions
Children believe that all measurement scales will come up with an accurate result.
Show the children examples, like one of those on the worksheet, where measurements come between markers and are therefore approximate. Also show them that the larger the intervals on the scale, the less accurately we are able to measure.

Probing questions
● Are you now confident about working out the value of unnumbered markers on a measurement scale?
● How can you estimate as accurately as possible the position of a measurement between the written markers on a scale?

Next steps
Support: Stress to children that when estimating they must decide which interval contains the measurement and then which side of the interval the measurement is nearer to. Refer back to Year 6 Block C Units 1 and 2.
Extension: Ask children to investigate, with the help of grocery packaging, the differences between the terms gross weight and net weight. Refer also to Year 6 Block D Units 1 and 3.

Activity ⑦

Prior learning
Children can solve problems with a calculator involving more than one step.

Framework objective
Use a calculator to solve problems involving multi-step calculations

Vocabulary
problem, solution, calculate, calculation, operation, answer, method, strategy, explain, reason, calculator, function, key, display, enter, clear

Resources
Interactive activity: Conversion graph
Resource sheet: Self-assessment
Classroom resources: calculators

⑦ Conversion graph

Using the interactive activity 'Conversion graph', present the children with a pre-set straight-line graph that converts between pounds and dollars based on the current exchange rate. (You will need to create this before the lesson, entering one currency in the first column and the other in the second column of the data table.) Ask the children a series of questions where they have to convert pounds into dollars (and vice versa) with a calculator, using the conversion graph to assist them. Make some of the questions difficult where, as money amounts, their answers have to be rounded to two decimal places. Decide whether to use the self-assessment sheet for the children to record their achievements and what they need to do next.

Teacher support
Less confident learners: Help these children with conversions where solutions provided by the calculator are awkward – for example, read £5.2 as £5.20 and read £10.9675 as £10.97.
More confident learners: Ask these children to create a similar graph for converting pounds to euros. Allow them to input all the data into the data table.

Common misconceptions
Children produce a 'nonsense' answer using the calculator but assume it must be correct.
Point out it is easy to make an error when keying in a number or operation, so children should always check their answer in another way.

Probing questions
● Would the calculation have been easier or quicker to do using another method?
● What method did you use to check your answer? Was it at least approximately correct?

Next steps
Support: Discuss with the children which they found easier – working out the answer just using the calculator or referring to the conversion graph. Refer back to Year 6 Block A Units 1, 2 and 3 and Block C Unit 2.
Extension: Get the children to work in pairs. Ask them to write down four digits along with one operation sign and the equals sign (for example, 1, 5, 3, 4, × =). Ask them to press the keys in whatever order they like to produce an answer (for example, 2155). Using a calculator, their partner must work out the order in which the keys were pressed. (431 × 5 = 2155) Refer also to Year 6 Block D Units 1, 2 and 3.

BLOCK C

Periodic assessment

These activities can be used at any time during the teaching of this block to assess those children that you think have achieved the objective. A grid highlighting the related assessment focuses and expected learning outcomes for each activity can be found on the CD-ROM.

Data handling

Framework objectives
Solve problems by collecting, selecting, processing, presenting and interpreting data, using ICT where appropriate; draw conclusions and identify further questions to ask. Describe and predict outcomes from data using the language of chance and likelihood

Learning outcomes
● I can use data to work out problems about chance.
● I can use the language of chance to solve problems.

Provide the children with copies of the worksheet 'Probability'. In this assessment activity the children are asked to answer three types of question relating to probabilities.

Mode, range, median and mean

Framework objective
Describe and interpret results and solutions using the mode, range, median and mean

Learning outcome
● I can work out different types of average.

Provide each child with a copy of the worksheet 'Number ranges'. In the first section of the sheet the children need to find the range, mode, median and mean of five sets of numbers, while in the second section they are asked to make up their own sets of numbers for which they must work out the range, mode, median and mean.

Metric units

Framework objective
Select and use standard metric units of measure and convert between units using decimals to two places

Learning outcomes
● I can convert from one unit of measure to another.
● I can convert measures between units including decimals.

Hand out copies of the worksheet 'Metric units' for the children to complete. They are required to carry out the conversion of metric units and sorting tasks, placing masses and capacities in the correct numerical order.

Name	Date

Probability

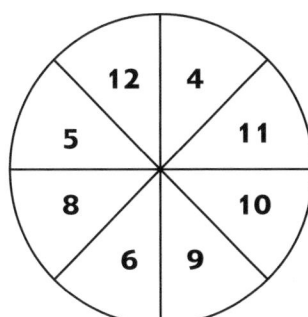

1. Using fractions and percentages, write the chances of getting the following numbers on this spinner.

a) an even number   _____   _____

b) an odd number   _____   _____

c) a prime number   _____   _____

d) a single-digit number   _____   _____

e) a square number   _____   _____

2. Mark the probability of each of the five events in question 1 in the most suitable place on the scale below. You may need to approximate. Label your arrows a, b, etc.

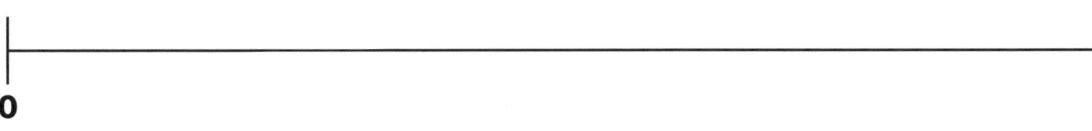

0   **1**

3. Make up two more questions of your own for probabilities to be placed on the scale.

_____

_____

_____

How easy?

Red

Amber

Green

How do you think you have done?

_____

_____

BLOCK C

Name	Date

Metric units

■ Put each of these sets of masses in order of size, smallest first.

1.   426g   0.47kg   0.046 tonne   4kg 250g   47g

_____   _____   _____   _____   _____

2.   550g   0.005 tonne   1.54kg   5kg 50g   5005g

_____   _____   _____   _____   _____

3.   650g   0.06 tonne   0.75kg   1.35kg   3kg 450g

_____   _____   _____   _____   _____

■ Put each of these sets of capacities in order of size, largest first.

4.   0.04l   304ml   35cl   3l 570ml   1.7l

_____   _____   _____   _____   _____

5.   1.23l   2l 310ml   315cl   3.2l   2131ml

_____   _____   _____   _____   _____

6.   4.6l   640ml   65cl   6l 400ml   4060ml

_____   _____   _____   _____   _____

How easy?

Red
Amber
Green

How do you think you have done?

_____

_____

BLOCK D
Calculating, measuring and understanding shape

Expected prior learning
Check that children can already:
- solve one- and two-step problems involving whole numbers and decimals, explaining their methods, and using a calculator where appropriate
- multiply and divide whole numbers and decimals by 10, 100 or 1000
- mentally multiply a two-digit by a one-digit number (e.g. 12 × 9) and multiply by 25 (e.g. 16 × 25)
- use efficient written methods to multiply and divide HTU × U, TU × TU, U.t × U and HTU ÷ U
- apply their knowledge of multiplication and division facts to estimate and check results
- use standard metric units to estimate and measure length, weight and capacity
- convert larger to smaller units using decimals to one place (e.g. change 2.6kg to 2600g)
- measure and calculate the perimeter of regular and irregular polygons; use the formula for the area of a rectangle to calculate its area
- read and plot coordinates in the first quadrant
- identify lines of symmetry in 2D shapes; draw the position of a shape after a reflection or translation
- estimate, draw and measure acute and obtuse angles using an angle measurer or protractor
- calculate angles on a straight line.

Objectives overview
The text in this diagram identifies the focus of mathematics learning within the block.

Key aspects of learning
- Enquiry
- Information processing
- Problem solving
- Evaluation

Metric units, conversions, imperial scales

Readings from scales

Solving multi-step problems, using a calculator where appropriate

Estimating and checking results

Estimating, measuring and drawing angles

Angle sum of a triangle; angles around a point

BLOCK D: Calculating, measuring and understanding shape

Calculation

Mental and written methods: integers and decimals, including HTU × TU

Area and perimeter of rectilinear shapes

Coordinates

Reflection, translation, rotation

Unit 1 ◻ Calculating, measuring and understanding shape

Introduction

The opening section of this nine-lesson unit deals with using and applying mathematics to solve word problems in practical settings. This is followed by revision of addition and subtraction strategies, often in situations involving money or metric measures. It also includes lessons dealing with multiplying decimal numbers, and division activities that produce remainders. Division using money also features, and children will find out that answers sometimes need to be rounded up or down. The unit ends with work on finding the perimeter and area of compound shapes.

Framework objectives	Assessment focuses		Success criteria for Year 6	Learning outcomes
	Level 5	Level 4		
① Train journey				
Solve multi-step problems, and problems involving fractions, decimals and percentages; choose and use appropriate calculation strategies at each stage, including calculator use	• identify and obtain necessary information to carry through a task and solve mathematical problems, e.g. • recognise information that is important to solving the problem, determine what is missing and develop lines of enquiry • break a several-step problem or investigation into simpler steps • consider efficient methods, relating problems to previous experiences	• develop own strategies for solving problems, e.g. • make their own suggestions of ways to tackle a range of problems • make connections to previous work • pose and answer questions related to a problem • check answers and ensure solutions make sense in the context of the problem • review their work and approaches	• can use appropriate strategies when solving problems • identifies and defines key words when solving word problems • can break up problem-solving tasks into simple steps • can find more than one strategy to solve a problem • develops lines of enquiry to set up problem-solving tasks	*I can solve problems with several steps and decide how to carry out the calculation.*
② Jumbled calculations				
Calculate mentally with integers and decimals: $U.t \pm U.t$, $TU \times U$, $TU \div U$, $U.t \times U$, $U.t \div U$	• use all four operations with decimals to two places, e.g. • add and subtract numbers that do not have the same number of decimal places • multiply or divide decimal numbers by a single digit, e.g. 31.62×7	• use a range of mental methods of computation with all operations, e.g. • calculate complements to 1000 • recall multiplication facts up to 10×10 and quickly derive corresponding division facts, e.g. • use their knowledge of tables and place value in calculations with multiples of 10 such as 30×7, $180 \div 3$	• can add, subtract, multiply and divide whole numbers and decimals mentally • can decide when working mentally is appropriate • explains what mental methods have been used to find answers • shows evidence that answers can be found in several different ways	*I can add, subtract, multiply and divide whole numbers and decimals in my head.*

BLOCK D

■SCHOLASTIC

Unit 1 ◻ Calculating, measuring and understanding shape

Framework objectives	Assessment focuses		Success criteria for Year 6	Learning outcomes
	Level 5	Level 4		
③ Eat at Marco's				
Use efficient written methods to add and subtract integers or decimals, to multiply and divide integers or decimals by a one-digit integer, and to multiply two-digit and three-digit integers by a two-digit integer	• understand and use an appropriate non-calculator method for solving problems that involve multiplying or dividing any three-digit number by any two-digit number	• use efficient written methods of addition and subtraction and of short multiplication and division, e.g. ● calculate 1202 + 45 + 367 or 1025 – 336 • add and subtract decimals to two places • multiply a simple decimal by a single digit, e.g. ● calculate 36.2 × 8	• knows when it is necessary to use efficient written methods • can add, subtract, multiply and divide whole numbers using efficient written methods • can add, subtract, multiply and divide decimal numbers using efficient written methods • describes to others written methods that have been used	*I can add, subtract, multiply and divide whole numbers and decimals using efficient written methods.*
④ Consecutive numbers				
Use a calculator to solve problems involving multi-step calculations	• use a calculator where appropriate to calculate fractions/percentages of quantities/measurements, e.g. ● find fractions of quantities such as 3/8 of 980 ● find percentages such as 15% of 360g	• use inverse operations, e.g. ● use a calculator and inverse operations to find missing numbers, including decimals • solve problems with or without a calculator	• knows when to use a calculator to work out a calculation • uses a calculator for carrying out multi-step calculations • can devise an appropriate strategy for working out a problem using a calculator • can solve a problem with a calculator using a trial and improvement method	*I can use a calculator to solve problems with several steps.*
⑤ Meet your match				
Use approximations, inverse operations and tests of divisibility to estimate and check results	• approximate to check answers to problems are of the correct magnitude • check solutions by applying inverse operations or estimating using approximations • check results, considering whether these are reasonable, e.g. ● check as they work, spotting and correcting errors and reviewing methods	• check the reasonableness of results with reference to the context or size of numbers • develop own strategies for solving problems, e.g. ● check answers and ensure solutions make sense in the context of the problem ● review their work and approaches	• knows how to round off decimal numbers when estimating answers • knows the importance of working out approximate answers when doing calculations • knows ways of checking answers when conclusion is reached (e.g. using inverse operation)	*I can estimate the result of a calculation.* *I know several ways of checking answers.*

BLOCK D

Unit 1 📖 Calculating, measuring and understanding shape

Framework objectives	Assessment focuses		Success criteria for Year 6	Learning outcomes
	Level 5	**Level 4**		
⑥ Handy measures				
Select and use standard metric units of measure and convert between units using decimals to two places (e.g. change 2.75 litres to 2750ml, or vice versa)	• solve problems involving the conversion of units, e.g. • solve problems such as 1.5kg ÷ 30g • work out approximately how many kilometres are equivalent to 20 miles	• choose and use appropriate units and instruments	• converts one unit of measures to another, using decimal numbers where appropriate • can estimate the weight/height/length, etc of certain items • is able to write the same metric measures in a number of different ways	I can convert one measurement to another using a related unit. I use decimals to do this.
⑦ All change (mass and capacity)				
Solve problems by measuring, estimating and calculating; measure and calculate using imperial units still in everyday use; know their approximate metric values	• solve problems involving the conversion of units, e.g. • work out approximately how many kilometres are equivalent to 20 miles • make sensible estimates of a range of measures in relation to everyday situations	There is no assessment focus for this level	• identifies and uses selected imperial measurements of weight and capacity • knows the approximate metric values of chosen imperial units • can appreciate situations where imperial units might still be used	I know that 1 pint is just over half a litre, and that 1 litre is about 1¾ pints. I know that 1 mile is about 1.6km, and that 1km is about 5/8 of a mile.
⑧ Draw the line				
Read and interpret scales on a range of measuring instruments, recognising that the measurement made is approximate and recording results to a required degree of accuracy; compare readings on different scales, for example when using different instruments	• read and interpret scales on a range of measuring instruments, explaining what each labelled division represents	• interpret, with appropriate accuracy, numbers on a range of measuring instruments, e.g. • measure a length using millimetres, to within 2mm	• can read scales on a variety of measuring instruments • explains what each labelled division represents on scales • can compare readings on different scales • can represent the same quantity on a range of different scales	I can read scales as accurately as a problem requires. I can compare readings from different scales.
⑨ Calculating perimeter				
Calculate the perimeter and area of rectilinear shapes; estimate the area of an irregular shape by counting squares	• understand and use the formula for the area of a rectangle and distinguish area from perimeter, e.g. • find the length of a rectangle given its perimeter and width • find the area or perimeter of simple L shapes, given some edge lengths	• find perimeters of simple shapes and find areas by counting squares, e.g. • use the terms 'area' and 'perimeter' accurately and consistently • find areas by counting squares and part squares	• can define the word perimeter when applied to shapes • understands that perimeter is about measuring distance • can find the perimeter of simple shapes • can use quick methods for calculating the perimeter of a shape	I can find the perimeter and area of shapes and estimate the area of irregular shapes.

BLOCK D

112

100 MATHS ASSESSMENT LESSONS · YEAR 6

■SCHOLASTIC

Unit 1 Calculating, measuring and understanding shape

Activity

Prior learning
Children can solve problems involving several steps and decide how to carry out calculations.

Framework objective
Solve multi-step problems, and problems involving decimals and percentages; choose and use appropriate calculation strategies at each stage, including calculator use

Vocabulary
problem, solution, answer, method, strategy, operation, calculation, calculate, calculator

Resources
Worksheet: Train journey
Classroom resources: calculators

① Train journey

Give the children copies of the worksheet 'Train journey'. They are asked to solve a simple problem involving train travel, carrying out several calculations in order to arrive at the solution. They must show all working out. Calculators should only be used to check the solution at the end.

Teacher support
Less confident learners: Some children may need to be reminded of the stages they need to go through in order to solve this type of word problem: read carefully, decide on operations, estimate the answer.
More confident learners: On the theme of rail travel, set these children further problems about the relative merits of buying either daily rail tickets or a season ticket.

Common misconceptions
Children think that most of the working out can be done mentally and it will save time not having to write down calculations.
Point out that writing down calculations will show helpers where they might be having problems. Also that in some test situations, showing their 'method' can earn marks even if their final solution is incorrect.

Probing questions
● What were the key words in the word problem that helped you to decide what calculations to carry out?
● How many different methods could you find to work out the solution?

Next steps
Support: Keep revising strategies for solving word problems so that children get into the habit of following an identical, reliable procedure every time. Refer back to Year 6 Block A Units 2 and 3.
Extension: Encourage children to be on the look out for everyday situations where calculations are needed to solve problems (for example, checking shopping bills, bus and rail travel or the cost of mobile telephone packages). Refer also to Year 6 Block E Units 1 and 3.

BLOCK D

Activity ②

Prior learning
Children can add, subtract, multiply and divide whole numbers and decimals mentally.

Framework objective
Calculate mentally with integers and decimals: U.t ± U.t, TU × U, TU ÷ U, U.t × U, U.t ÷ U

Vocabulary
integer, decimal, decimal point, decimal place, add, subtract, multiply, divide, mentally

Resources
Worksheet: Jumbled calculations

② Jumbled calculations

This task can be carried out either individually or in small groups. Give out the worksheet 'Jumbled calculations'. Explain that the circles and triangles are in the correct places but the squares have been jumbled up. The children have to draw lines to match up each of the squares (a number with an operation sign) with a circle in order to make the correct answer in the triangle. Set no time limit on this activity as some children may need to use trial and improvement methods to arrive at the correct solution.

Teacher support
Less confident learners: Encourage these children to work out the problems involving whole numbers first and to cross out numbers as they are used to reduce the choice.
More confident learners: Ask pairs of children to devise their own activities like this that they can test out on each other.

Common misconceptions
Children assume that because they are looking for solutions mentally there is only one way in which to solve the problem.
Following the activity discuss, in some detail, the way in which answers were calculated. Try to find at least two or three different strategies that can be used to find the answer.

Probing questions
● Which questions were most difficult to do? Which were the easiest? Explain why.
● What mental strategies could be used to check that your solutions were correct?

Next steps
Support: Give children plenty of experience of activities of this kind. The more mental activities they are encouraged to take part in, the more proficient they will become. Refer back to Year 6 Block A Units 1, 2 and 3.
Extension: Devise a game in which three number statements have been combined in order to produce the answer, ie the squares, circles and triangles are all jumbled up. Refer also to Year 6 Block D Units 2 and 3.

Activity

Prior learning
Children can add, subtract, multiply and divide whole numbers and decimals using efficient written methods.

Framework objective
Use efficient written methods to add and subtract integers and decimals, to multiply and divide integers and decimals by a one-digit integer, and to multiply two- and three-digit integers by a two-digit integer

Vocabulary
calculate, calculation, operation, answer, method, strategy, jotting, explain, place value, digit, number, integer, decimal point, decimal place, round up, round down

Resources
Worksheet: Eat at Marco's
Classroom resources: multiplication squares (for support)

③ Eat at Marco's

This activity tests children's ability to use written methods to divide three-digit integers by one- or two-digit integers. Provide the children with copies of the worksheet 'Eat at Marco's'. The questions given are set in a money context and, in the last three questions, the children need to consider remainders so that answers are given to the nearest pound. They should not use calculators and should show all their working.

Teacher support
Less confident learners: These children may need some guidance and explanation to help them with rounding off the last three answers to the nearest £.
More confident learners: In the last three questions on the worksheet, challenge these children to find out more accurately how much each of the guests would have to pay.

Common misconceptions
Children become confused about the best way of writing down their working when they are using more formal written methods.
Revise written methods of working with the children frequently. It may also help to have enlarged versions of calculations on display in the classroom for reference purposes.

Probing questions
● Which did you find easier, working the division problems horizontally inside the bracket or setting numbers down in vertical columns?
● How did you decide, in the last three questions, whether to round remainders up or down to the nearest £?

Next steps
Support: The children may need multiplication squares if they have difficulty with some of the division questions. Refer back to Year 6 Block A Units 2 and 3.
Extension: Ask children to use the inverse operation (in this case multiplication) to check that their answers are correct. Refer also to Year 6 Block D Units 2 and 3, Block E Units 1 and 3.

BLOCK D

Activity ④

Framework objective
Use a calculator to solve problems including multi-step calculations

Vocabulary
problem, solution, calculate, calculation, operation, answer, method, strategy, explain, reason, calculator, function, key, display, enter, clear

Resources
Resource sheet: Self-assessment
Classroom resources: calculators

④ Consecutive numbers

Provide each child with a calculator. The activity this time is more in the nature of an investigation. Encourage the children to work towards the solution using a trial and improvement method. The use of the calculator will mean that a large number of calculations can be carried out quickly.

Task 1: The number 9177 has been made by multiplying three consecutive odd numbers. Which numbers have been used? (19, 21, 23)

Task 2: The number 17,472 has been made by multiplying three consecutive even numbers. What are they? (24, 26, 28)

When the children have completed this activity, decide whether to use the self-assessment sheet so that they can record their achievements and next steps.

Teacher support
Less confident learners: Encourage these children to approach the problems by multiplying identical numbers to get them started. For example, in the first task 20 × 20 × 20 = 8000 would be a start.

More confident learners: Challenge these children to set similar problems for other children to solve.

Common misconceptions
Children feel that they cannot solve the problem because they are uncertain about what numbers to start entering into the calculator.
Boost confidence by telling the children that any number investigation needs to start somewhere and that the problem will become easier once they have made a start.

Probing questions
● Did you find the solution by trial and improvement, or during the course of the task did you see combinations of numbers that lead you from one answer to another?
● When did it become evident that the solution to the problem would be three consecutive odd/even numbers in that number range?

Next steps
Support: As a number of calculations need to be carried out, make sure that the children are clearing answers from the calculator before starting a new calculation. Refer back to Year 6 Block A Units 1, 2 and 3, Block B Units 2 and 3, Block C Units 2 and 3.

Extension: Challenge children to make words on the calculator. For example, 5537 upside down will produce the word LESS. The longest that can be displayed have eight letters – for example, 77345993 is EGGSHELL. Refer also to Year 6 Block D Units 2 and 3, Block E Units 1, 2 and 3.

Activity ⑤

Prior learning
Children can round off decimal numbers to the nearest whole number and estimate the result of a calculation.

Framework objective
Use approximation, inverse operations and tests of divisibility to estimate and check results

Vocabulary
digit, numeral, integer, decimal point, decimal place, whole number, round, estimate, approximate, approximately, multiply

Resources
Interactive activity: Meet your match
Classroom resources: calculators

⑤ Meet your match

In the interactive activity 'Meet your match', children have to round the decimal numbers in the problems column, multiply them together and then use the product to help them find the correct solution in the other column. They should use calculators to check that their selections are correct. All the answers have been rounded to two decimal places.

Teacher support
Less confident learners: Ensure that these children fully appreciate the place value of the numbers involved. Tell them to make a point of noting carefully where the units digit is in each case.
More confident learners: Make tasks more difficult by working with amounts where rounding becomes more difficult because the decimal numbers come about half way between two whole numbers (for example, rounding 7.56 and 12.63).

Common misconceptions
Children think that rounding, especially with decimal numbers, produces an answer that is of little assistance because it is too far away from the actual answer.
Point out that an answer found by rounding decimal numbers is particularly useful in showing whether the decimal point is correctly positioned in the actual answer (for example, that the actual answer is closer to 8, 80 or 800).

Probing questions
● Explain to me how to round numbers containing two decimal places to the nearest whole number.
● Is there another way of checking the answer to see if the calculation is correct?

Next steps
Support: Talk children through a second way in which the answers could be checked: in this case, checking multiplication calculations by using the inverse operation (division). Refer back to Year 6 Block A Units 1, 2 and 3, Block B Units 1, 2 and 3.
Extension: Think of practical examples where being able to multiply decimal numbers would be useful – for example, finding the area of rectangles with awkward dimensions, such as 4.17m × 3.9m, or calculating money amounts, such as £3.75 × 4. Refer also to Year 6 Block D Units 2 and 3.

Activity ⑥

Prior learning
Children can convert one measurement to another using a related unit. They can use decimals to carry out this process.

Framework objective
Select and use standard metric units of measure and convert between units using decimals to two places (for example, change 2.75 litres to 2750ml, or vice versa)

Vocabulary
estimate, measure, convert, change, unit, gram (g), kilogram (kg), tonne (t), litre (l), millilitre (ml), centilitre (cl), millimetre (mm), centimetre (cm), metre (m), kilometre (km)

Resources
Worksheet: Handy measures
Classroom resources: apples, buckets, eggcups, lumps of sugar, sheets of A4 paper; rulers, measuring tapes, scales

⑥ Handy measures

Provide each group of children with copies of the worksheet 'Handy measures' and the five objects listed under Classroom resources (see above). They are asked to estimate the capacity, mass and length/height of the items listed on the sheet, giving their answers using two different kinds of metric units. The answers should then be checked by accurate measuring.

Teacher support
Less confident learners: Give these children plenty of hands-on measuring activities in which they get practice in estimating the capacity, mass and length of common objects.
More confident learners: Expect these children to get closer to the actual measurements. Institute a scoring system in which more points are scored the closer they get to the actual answers.

Common misconceptions
Children forget to include the correct number of zeros as place-holders when writing small amounts in larger units (for example, 50g in kilograms becomes 0.050kg).
Provide children with place-value charts initially and make sure that every column is filled in and none left blank.

Probing questions
● Which type of metric units do you have most trouble converting: capacity, mass or length/height?
● How can you select the most practical type of metric units to be used for measuring stated items? (For example, a bath of water could be measured in millilitres but litres would be more sensible; a bed could be measured in millimetres but metres and centimetres would be more sensible.)

Next steps
Support: Keep emphasising that it is much easier to compare metric measurements if they are put into the same units. For example, 450ml, 0.5 litres and 3 litres 250ml are better considered as 450ml, 500ml and 3250ml. Refer back to Year 6 Block C Units 1, 2 and 3.
Extension: See how good children are at estimating the approximate capacity/mass/length of very small and very large items (for example, capacity of a teaspoon and a bath; mass of a teabag and of a friend; width of a postage stamp and length of the playground). Refer also to Year 6 Block D Units 2 and 3.

Activity ⑦

Prior learning
Children can name imperial units still in use and give their approximate metric equivalents (for example, 1 pint is just over half a litre).

Framework objective
Solve problems by measuring, estimating and calculating; measure and calculate using imperial units still in everyday use; know their approximate metric values

Vocabulary
metric units, imperial units, estimate, approximate, pint, millilitre, litre, pound, ounce, gram, kilogram, convert

Resources
Interactive activity: All change (mass and capacity)
Classroom resources: calculators

⑦ All change (mass and capacity)

Reveal the interactive activity 'All change (mass and capacity)'. In this activity, the children are required to match up equivalent items labelled in metric and imperial units. The first screen matches pounds to kilograms, while the second screen matches litres to pints. The children can find more exact results later by using a calculator and the conversions 1lb = 0.4536kg and 1 litre = 1.759 pints.

Teacher support
Less confident learners: These children will need support with multiplying even when approximate equivalents are being found.
More confident learners: As suggested above, encourage these children to use a calculator to work out the exact calculations. Answers should be rounded to two decimal places.

Common misconceptions
Children cannot see the value of learning about imperial units when metric units are in common use throughout the country.
Assure the children that some items are still measured in imperial units in this country, particularly mass, and that in some countries (such as the United States of America) imperial units are still the main units of measurement.

Probing questions
● How close did your approximate conversion answer get to the answer you worked out on the calculator? Was the estimate a useful rough guide?
● How difficult do you find it to appreciate quantities given in imperial units when you are dealing with metric units most of the time?

Next steps
Support: Display conversion charts and facts about imperial and metric units in the classroom when children are working on these tasks.
Extension: Encourage children to carry out some research into imperial units in the measurement of length and distance (for example, inches, feet, yards and miles). These will feature in Year 6 Block D Unit 3.

BLOCK D

Activity ⑧

Prior learning Children can read scales as accurately as a problem requires. They can compare readings from different scales.	**Framework objective** Read and interpret scales on a range of measuring instruments, recognising that the measurement made is approximate, and recording results to a required degree of accuracy; compare readings on different scales, for example when using different instruments **Vocabulary** estimate, approximate, scale, division, interval, capacity, weight, millilitre (ml), centilitre (cl), litre (l), gram (g), kilogram (kg) **Resources** **Worksheet:** Draw the line **Classroom resources:** pencils, rulers

⑧ Draw the line

Provide the children with copies of the worksheet 'Draw the line' on which four containers are labelled with different scales. The children have to mark the levels of water stated for each of the containers with a straight line.

Teacher support
Less confident learners: Label some of the unlabelled intervals on each of the scales to help these children decide where the water level should be drawn.
More confident learners: Give these children similar problems using the same set of measuring containers. Again, set questions with amounts in either millilitres or litres.

Common misconceptions
Children assume that all intervals shown on a measuring scale are actually marked with numbers.
Point out that there is often not room to do this and that usually only important points are marked on the scale.

Probing questions
● Which was easier – having the level marks on the containers given in litres or millilitres?
● Which was the most difficult of the three containers to mark? Which of the scales was easiest to read?

Next steps
Support: Make sure the children are familiar with litre measures marked in intervals of 100ml before moving on to more difficult scales. Refer back to Year 6 Block C Units 1, 2 and 3.
Extension: Devise questions involving levels that come between interval markers so that children have to use their estimation skills as well. Refer also to Year 6 Block D Unit 3.

BLOCK D

■SCHOLASTIC

Activity ⑨

Prior learning
Children can find the perimeter of regular shapes.

Framework objective
Calculate the perimeter of rectilinear shapes; estimate the area of an irregular shape by counting squares

Vocabulary
measure, estimate, distance, length, width, perimeter, area, surface area, standard units, millimetres (mm), centimetres (cm), metres (m)

Resources
Interactive activity: Calculating perimeter

⑨ Calculating perimeter

Show the children the interactive activity 'Calculating perimeter'. The object of this activity is to demonstrate to the children that there is a quicker way of calculating perimeter than just finding the distance all the way round a shape. Use the whiteboard tool to build up rectangles of different sizes and shapes. Rather than telling the children that the perimeter is the sum of twice the length plus twice the width, see if they can discover this for themselves. Encourage the children to investigate the areas and perimeters of a range of different shapes on the grid.

Teacher support
Less confident learners: To begin with, allow these children to find the length all the way round a rectangle to ensure that they understand the concept of perimeter.
More confident learners: Ask these children to think of ways in which they could find the perimeter more quickly than adding lengths all the way round the shape.

Common misconceptions
Children become confused about the difference between perimeter and area.
Children should be given enough practical experience to help them to realise that perimeter (distance) is a one-dimensional attribute and that area (surface) is two dimensional.

Probing questions
● Suggest a quick way of finding the perimeter of a rectangle.
● If the perimeter is twice the length plus twice the width, is there another way of making the same calculation?

Next steps
Support: Keep reminding children that as perimeter is a measurement of distance, the standard units to use are centimetres, metres and kilometres. Refer back to Year 5 Block D Unit 2.
Extension: Make sure that these children experience activities that allow them to find the perimeter of large items, such as the classroom, the school hall, the playground, the field. Refer also to Year 6 Block D Unit 3.

BLOCK D

Unit 2 ▨ Calculating, measuring and understanding shape

Introduction
The beginning of this unit provides further opportunities to use and apply mathematical skills to solve word problems. Children then develop their ability to use written methods of calculation involving multiplying three-digit by two-digit integers and dividing a three-digit integer by a two-digit integer. This is followed by three lessons on angles, providing the opportunity to use a protractor and to calculate the internal angles of a triangle. There are two lessons on the use of coordinates, and the unit ends with activities involving reflecting shapes.

Framework objectives	Assessment focuses		Success criteria for Year 6	Learning outcomes
	Level 5	Level 4		
① Flowerbed				
Solve multi-step problems, and problems involving fractions, decimals and percentages; choose and use appropriate calculation strategies at each stage, including calculator use	● identify and obtain necessary information to carry through a task and solve mathematical problems, e.g. ● recognise information that is important to solving the problem, determine what is missing and develop lines of enquiry ● break a several-step problem or investigation into simpler steps ● consider efficient methods, relating problems to previous experiences	● develop own strategies for solving problems, e.g. ● make their own suggestions of ways to tackle a range of problems ● make connections to previous work ● pose and answer questions related to a problem ● check answers and ensure solutions make sense in the context of the problem ● review their work and approaches	● uses appropriate strategies when solving problems ● identifies and defines key vocabulary when solving word problems ● can break up problems into smaller, simpler steps ● can find more than one method for solving a problem ● can explain orally how they went about solving a problem	*I can solve problems with several steps and decide how to carry out the calculation.*
② Quick snack				
Calculate mentally with integers and decimals: U.t ± U.t, TU × U, TU ÷ U, U.t × U, U.t ÷ U	● use all four operations with decimals to two places, eg ● add and subtract numbers that do not have the same number of decimal places ● multiply or divide decimal numbers by a single digit, e.g. 31.62 × 7	● use a range of mental methods of computation with all operations, e.g. ● calculate complements to 1000 ● recall multiplication facts up to 10 × 10 and quickly derive corresponding division facts, e.g. ● use their knowledge of tables and place value in calculations with multiples of 10 such as 30 × 7, 180 ÷ 3	● can add, subtract, multiply and divide whole numbers and decimals mentally ● can give reasons why particular methods were chosen ● can show evidence that answers can be found by different methods	*I can add, subtract, multiply and divide whole numbers and decimals in my head.*

BLOCK D

Unit 2 📖 Calculating, measuring and understanding shape

Framework objectives	Assessment focuses		Success criteria for Year 6	Learning outcomes
	Level 5	**Level 4**		
③ Most efficient?				
Use efficient written methods to add or subtract integers or decimals, to multiply or divide integers or decimals by a one-digit integer, and to multiply two-digit or three-digit integers by a two-digit integer	• understand and use an appropriate non-calculator method for solving problems that involve multiplying and dividing any three-digit number by any two-digit number	• use efficient written methods of addition and subtraction and of short multiplication and division, e.g. ○ calculate 1202 + 45 + 367 or 1025 − 336 • add and subtract decimals to two places • multiply a simple decimal by a single digit, e.g. ○ calculate 36.2 × 8	• can explain why one written method was preferred to another • chooses the method that best fits the question • selects the method they are most comfortable working with	*I can add, subtract, multiply and divide whole numbers and decimals using efficient written methods.*
④ Twenty-three				
Use a calculator to solve problems involving multi-step calculations	• use a calculator where appropriate to calculate fractions/percentages of quantities/measurements, e.g. ○ find fractions of quantities such as 3/8 of 980 ○ find percentages such as 15% of 360g	• use inverse operations, e.g. ○ use a calculator and inverse operations to find missing numbers, including decimals • solve problems with or without a calculator	• knows when to use a calculator to work out a calculation • knows which function keys to use on a calculator • can explain why using a calculator has distinct advantages in some cases	*I can use a calculator to solve problems with several steps.*
⑤ Grand Hotel				
Use approximations, inverse operations and tests of divisibility to estimate and check results	• approximate to check that answers to problems are of the correct magnitude • check solutions by applying inverse operations or estimating using approximations • check results, considering whether these are reasonable, e.g. ○ check as they work, spotting and correcting errors and reviewing methods	• check the reasonableness of results with reference to the context or size of numbers • develop own strategies for solving problems, e.g. ○ check answers and ensure solutions make sense in the context of the problem ○ review their work and approaches	• can use approximations to work out calculations and also to check results • is aware of the fact that approximating and estimating can often prevent mistakes being made	*I can estimate the result of a calculation.* *I know several ways of checking answers.*
⑥ Kitchen units				
Select and use standard metric units of measure and convert between units using decimals to two places (e.g. change 2.75 litres to 2750ml, or vice versa)	• solve problems involving the conversion of units, e.g. ○ solve problems such as 1.5kg ÷ 30g ○ work out approximately how many kilometres are equivalent to 20 miles	• choose and use appropriate units and instruments	• can convert one unit of measurement to another using decimal numbers where appropriate • knows the importance of using zero as a place-holder when writing metric units • can carry out calculations that involve the conversion of metric units	*I can convert a measurement in one unit to another using a related unit.* *I use decimals to do this.*

BLOCK D

Unit 2 ▣ Calculating, measuring and understanding shape

Framework objectives	Assessment focuses		Success criteria for Year 6	Learning outcomes
	Level 5	**Level 4**		
⑦ Calculating angles				
Estimate angles, and use a protractor to measure and draw them, on their own and in shapes; calculate angles in a triangle or around a point	● know and use the angle sum of a triangle and that of angles at a point, e.g. ● calculate angles on a straight line or at a point such as the angle between the hands of a clock, or intersecting diagonals at the centre of a regular hexagon ● measure and draw angles to the nearest degree, when constructing models and drawing or using shapes, e.g. ● measure and draw reflex angles to the nearest degree, when neither edge is horizontal/vertical ● construct a triangle given the length of two sides and the angle between them (accurate to 1mm and 2°) ● use language associated with angle	● interpret, with appropriate accuracy, numbers on a range of measuring instruments, e.g. ● measure and draw acute and obtuse angles to the nearest 5°, when one edge is horizontal/ vertical	● can name the main angle families ● can estimate the size of angles ● uses a protractor to draw and measure angles ● knows the angles in the triangle sum to 180° ● knows the angles round a point sum to 360° ● knows language associated with angles	*I can estimate angles, and use a protractor to measure and draw them.* *I know that the angle sum of a triangle is 180° and the sum of angles around a point is 360°.*
⑧ Join up				
Use coordinates in the first quadrant to draw, locate and complete shapes that meet given properties	● use and interpret coordinates in all four quadrants	● use and interpret coordinates in the first quadrant	● uses and interprets coordinates in all four quadrants ● can draw shapes using coordinates ● appreciates situations in which coordinates are used practically (e.g. maps)	*I can use coordinates when the x-coordinate and the y-coordinate are both positive.*
⑨ Finding reflections ⑩ Finding rotations				
Visualise and draw on grids of different types where a shape will be after reflection, after translations, or after rotation through 90° or 180° about its centre or one of its vertices	● transform shapes, e.g. ● reflect shapes in oblique (45°) mirror lines where the shape either does not touch the mirror line, or where the shape crosses the mirror line ● reflect shapes not presented on grids, by measuring perpendicular distances to/from the mirror ● reflect shapes in two mirror lines, where the shape is not parallel or perpendicular to either mirror ● rotate shapes, through 90° or 180°, when the centre of rotation is a vertex of the shape, and recognise such rotations ● translate shapes along an oblique line	● reflect simple shapes in a mirror line, e.g. ● use a grid to plot the reflection in a mirror line presented at 45° where the shape touches the line or not ● begin to use the distance of vertices from the mirror line to reflect shapes more accurately ● begin to rotate a simple shape or object about its centre or a vertex ● translate shapes horizontally or vertically	● can draw on a grid where a shape will be after reflection ● can draw on a grid where a shape will be after rotation ● can draw on a grid where a shape will be after translation	*I can reflect, rotate and translate shapes on grids.*

◼ SCHOLASTIC

Activity ①

Prior learning
Children can solve problems with several steps and decide how to carry out the calculation.

Framework objective
Solve multi-step problems and problems involving decimals; choose and use appropriate calculation strategies at each stage, including calculator use

Vocabulary
problem, solution, answer, method, strategy, operation, calculation, calculate, decimal, decimal point, decimal place, add, subtract, multiply, divide, sum, total, difference, plus

Resources
Worksheet: Flowerbed

① Flowerbed

Provide the children with copies of the worksheet 'Flowerbed'. Explain that they need to solve several problems based on a real-life setting involving a flowerbed in a park. They should record their working out on the sheet and should only use calculators to check their answer at the end.

Teacher support
Less confident learners: Provide a framework that the children can use to find their way to the correct solution. It may be necessary to break down the problem into sections so they can be calculated one stage at a time.
More confident learners: With problems of this kind, ask the children to talk through the various stages of the process, explaining to others their reasoning behind approaching the problem in a certain way.

Common misconceptions
Children are under the impression that there is only one method for finding the answer and that a set formula needs to be used every time.
Encourage these children to be flexible in their approach to problem-solving so that they are capable of reaching a solution by exploring a number of different routes.

Probing questions
● How did you first get started on the problem? What advice would you give to anyone on the best way in?
● Which part of the problem did you find most difficult? Was it the section involving dimensions or calculating the amounts of money being spent?

Next steps
Support: Encourage children to ask adults at home to provide them with simple problems of this nature to solve so that they get used to encountering situations like this in context. Refer back to Year 6 Block A Units 2 and 3, Block D Unit 1.
Extension: Provide children with a catalogue or price list from a garden centre or building merchants so that they can devise their own measuring and money problems involving paving stones and slabs. Refer also to Year 6 Block D Unit 3.

BLOCK D

Activity ②

Prior learning
Children can add, subtract, multiply and divide whole numbers and decimals in their heads.

Framework objective
Calculate mentally with integers and decimals: U.t ± U.t, TU × U, TU ÷ U, U.t × U, U.t ÷ U

Vocabulary
integer, decimal, decimal point, decimal place, add, subtract, multiply, divide, mentally

Resources
Display page: Quick snack
Resource sheet: Self-assessment

② Quick snack

Show the children the display page 'Quick snack'. Tell them to study the snack bar tariff and then ask them the following questions:
1. What is the cost of a tea and a burger? (£1.10)
2. What is the cost of two coffees and a hot dog? (£1.50)
3. What is the difference in price between a burger and a sausage roll? (20p)
4. Find the cost of five coffees. (£2.50)
5. Find the cost of four teas and one sausage roll. (£1.80)
6. How much change is there from £5 after buying three burgers and a squash? (£2.40)
7. What is the least number of coins you could use to buy a sausage roll and a tea? (3: 50p, 20p, 20p)
8. If four packets of crisps cost £1.60, how much do they cost each? (40p)
The children should work through all the questions mentally and be prepared to explain what mental strategies and calculations they carried out in order to solve the problems. Decide whether to use the self-assessment sheet for the children to record their achievements and what they need to do next.

Teacher support
Less confident learners: These children may need some easier questions to start them off. For example: *What is the cost of a tea and a coffee?*
More confident learners: Expect these children to be able to give several explanations as to how they arrived at the correct answer.

Common misconceptions
Children become set in their ways and want to try to use the same method of mental calculation each time.
Encourage these children to use different methods and see if they come up with the same answer.

Probing questions
● Which type of question did you find most difficult to calculate mentally: add, subtract, multiply or divide?
● Were you able to do a rough estimate of the answer first to see if you were more or less on the right lines?

Next steps
Support: Make sure that these children are secure with working with two items from the snack bar tariff first before moving on to more complex problems. Refer back to Year 6 Block A Units 1, 2 and 3, Block D Unit 1.
Extension: Set up other shopping and costing-type scenarios so that the children become used to working with money mentally in a number of different contexts. Refer also to Year 6 Block D Unit 3.

Activity ③

Prior learning
Children can add, subtract, multiply and divide whole numbers and decimals using efficient written methods.

Framework objective
Use efficient written methods to add and subtract integers and decimals, to multiply and divide integers and decimals by a one-digit integer, and to multiply two-digit and three-digit integers by a two-digit integer

Vocabulary
calculate, calculation, operation, answer, method, strategy, jotting, explain, place value, digit, number, integer, decimal point, decimal place

Resources
Display page: Most efficient?
Resource sheet: Self-assessment

③ Most efficient?

Go through the display page 'Most efficient?' on the screen, so that the children are able to see the three alternative written methods for multiplying a three-digit number by a two-digit number (long multiplication, the grid method and the lattice method). Ask them for their views on the advantages or disadvantages of each method. Ask: *Which do you think is the most efficient method? Why?* Decide whether to use the self-assessment sheet for the children to record their achievements and what they need to do next.

Teacher support
Less confident learners: Ask these children just to focus on the method they are most familiar with and explain why they think it is an efficient way of working.
More confident learners: Are these children able to find a further way of working out the same problem that may be more efficient still?

Common misconceptions
Children think that the first method they have been shown is the one they should stick to all the time.
Encourage these children to be more open-minded and to use either the method that fits the question best or the method they feel most comfortable using.

Probing questions
● When doing multiplications involving three-digit numbers, which columns should be dealt with first: units, tens or hundreds?
● How important is the use of answer boxes and diagrams in each of the three methods discussed? Why?

Next steps
Support: When children work on their own versions of this type of multiplication calculation, it may be necessary to provide pre-printed grids and boxes for them to work in. Refer back to Year 6 Block A Units 2 and 3.
Extension: Investigate other methods of multiplying numbers of this size, such as the Egyptian and Russian methods, which involve doubling in the first case and doubling and halving in the second. Refer also to Year 6 Block D Unit 3.

BLOCK D

Activity ④

Prior learning
Children can use a calculator to solve problems with several steps.

Framework objective
Use a calculator to solve problems involving multi-step calculations

Vocabulary
problem, solution, calculate, calculation, operation, answer, method, strategy, explain, reason, calculator, function, key, display, enter, clear

Resources
Resource sheet: Self-assessment
Classroom resources: calculators

④ Twenty-three

Present the children with this puzzle: *Put a four-digit number into the calculator. Add 25, multiply by 2, subtract 4 and divide by 2. Then subtract the original number. What is the answer?* (23) Challenge the children to try this out with different four-digit numbers. Decide whether to use the self-assessment sheet for the children to record their achievements and what they need to do next.

Teacher support
Less confident learners: Some children may find the problem easier if they press the = key between each of the stages to split up the task into small steps.
More confident learners: Encourage these children to investigate why the answer is always 23.

Common misconceptions
Children assume that all calculators they might use carry out operations in exactly the same way.
Arithmetic calculators perform each operation in the order you press the keys (for example, $2 + 5 \times 6 = (2 + 5) \times 6 = 42$). Algebraic calculators perform the multiplication first, using the BIDMAS rule – for this example, $2 + (5 \times 6) = 2 + 30 = 32$.

Probing questions
● In what way is it an advantage to use a calculator for this kind of problem?
● Would it be easier and quicker to carry out the calculations using some form of written method? Why?

Next steps
Support: Make sure that the children experience a number of simple calculator problem-solving tasks so that they become more skilled at using the device. Refer back to Year 6 Block A Units 1, 2 and 3, Block B Units 2 and 3, Block C Units 2 and 3.
Extension: Invite the children to try this puzzle: enter any three figures in a straight line on the calculator display (for example, 852). Press the addition key and then enter the same three figures, but this time reading in the opposite direction (ie 258). Find the total. Repeat for other lines of three numbers, always going through the centre of the display each time (the number 5). What do the children notice about the totals? (The answer is always 1110). Refer also to Year 6 Block D Unit 3.

Activity ⑤

Prior learning
Children can estimate the result of a calculation and know several ways of checking the answer.

Framework objective
Use approximations, inverse operations and tests of divisibility to estimate and check results

Vocabulary
digit, numeral, number, integer, decimal point, decimal place, whole number, round, estimate, approximate, approximately, multiply

Resources
Interactive activity: Grand Hotel
Classroom resources: calculators

⑤ Grand Hotel

Introduce the interactive activity 'Grand Hotel'. The items mentioned on the screen are based on goods that a staff member has to buy for the hotel. Tell the children that they first have to choose the best method of estimating the cost of each item, and then they show the actual cost. Answers should be confirmed by using the inverse operation (in this case, dividing). Calculators could then be used to confirm the solution.

Teacher support
Less confident learners: Encourage these children to practise estmating in different contexts.
More confident learners: Challenge these children to find another way of checking their answers.

Common misconceptions
Children think that rounding numbers and estimating is a waste of time and it is better to get straight on with the calculation.
Remind children that estimating is an integral part of the process of calculation and can often prevent problems from occurring later.

Probing questions
● How did you arrive at the estimated answer?
● Did you expect the answer to be greater or less than the estimate? Why?

Next steps
Support: Reward children with a points system: the closer they get to an answer when estimating, the more they score. Refer back to Year 6 Block A Units 1, 2 and 3, Block B Units 1, 2 and 3, Block D Unit 1.
Extension: Set the activity without the use of a calculator, using efficient written methods. Refer also to Year 6 Block D Unit 3.

BLOCK D

Activity ⑥

Prior learning	**Framework objective**
Children can convert a measurement in one unit to another using a related unit and decimals to do this.	**Select and use standard metric units of measure and convert between units using decimals to two places (for example, change 2.75 litres to 2750ml, and vice versa)**

Vocabulary
estimate, measure, convert, change, units, gram (g), kilogram (kg), tonne (t), litre (l), millilitre (ml), centilitre (cl), millimetre (mm), centimetre (cm), metre (m), kilometre (km)

Resources
Worksheet: Kitchen units

⑥ Kitchen units

Give out copies of the worksheet 'Kitchen units'. Ask the children to find out how certain units will fit into a newly designed kitchen. They have to convert the measurements of length into metres and centimetres using a decimal point.

Teacher support
Less confident learners: Make sure that these children are aware of the fact that one centimetre is one hundredth of a metre (ie 1cm = 0.01m).
More confident learners: Set practical measuring tasks around the classroom, in which dimensions have to be written in cm and m (for example, the length of the table is 90cm or 0.9m).

Common misconceptions
Children forget the importance of the zero as a place-holder when converting metric units, especially when converting from smaller units into larger ones. Give children plenty of examples of where this happens in practical measuring tasks. For example, 25cm = 0.25m and 3cm = 0.03m.

Probing questions
● How would you write 5m and 6cm as a decimal number?
● How would you write the decimal number 7.09m in centimetres?

Next steps
Support: Use display cards around the classroom showing key examples of conversion methods (for example, 36cm = 0.36m, 218cm = 2m 18cm, 2m 8cm = 2.08m). Refer back to Year 6 Block C Units 1, 2 and 3.
Extension: Assess children's conversion skills when they are asked to multiply and divide distances in problems. For example, 47cm × 9 (answer in metres) and 10.64m ÷ 7 (answer in centimetres). Refer also to Year 6 Block D Unit 3.

Activity ⑦

Prior learning
Children can estimate angles and use a protractor to measure and draw them. They know the angle sum of a triangle is 180° and the sum of the angles around a point is 360°.

Framework objective
Estimate angles and use a protractor to measure and draw them, on their own and in shapes; calculate angles in a triangle or around a point

Vocabulary
angle, degree (°), angle measurer, protractor, acute angle, right angle, obtuse angle, reflex angle

Resources
Interactive activity (ITP): Calculating angles
Resource sheet: Self-assessment

⑦ Calculating angles

Let the children use the ITP 'Calculating angles' to measure a variety of angles, either within a shape or on a 180° line. Decide whether to use the self-assessment sheet to record achievements and next steps.

Teacher support
Less confident learners: Consolidate measuring an angle around a point using a single shape on a 180° base line only.
More confident learners: Select the top item under the 'angle' button, which shows a circle. Begin measuring and estimating angles within this.

Common misconceptions
Children believe the angle size depends on the length of the arms of the angle. Provide angles that have different-sized arms, always stressing that an angle is not about length but about the amount of turn between two lines.

Probing questions
● When multiples of a regular shape are used (for example, an equilateral triangle), what happens to the outside angle? Is there a pattern?
● Are there any shapes we already know the angles of? If so, what are they?

Next steps
Support: Provide children with as much practice of using a protractor as possible, both with drawing and measuring angles of different kinds.
Extension: Challenge these children to draw pairs of intersecting angles and to measure the angles they form. What do they notice?

Activity ⑧

Prior learning
Children can use coordinates when the x-coordinate and the y-coordinate are both positive.

Framework objective
Use coordinates in the first quadrant to draw, locate and complete shapes that meet given properties

Vocabulary
coordinates, *x*-coordinate, *y*-coordinate, *x* axis, *y* axis, axes, quadrant, vertex, vertices

Resources
Worksheet: Join up

BLOCK D

⑧ Join up

Provide the children with copies of the worksheet 'Join up', which shows a coordinate grid numbered 1–10 on the *y* axis and 1–10 on the *x* axis. Ask the children to give the coordinates of three points (labelled A, B and C), complete the drawing of the rectangle and give the coordinates of the fourth vertex (D).

Teacher support
Less confident learners: Make sure that these children are certain about the correct way to write the position of a marker using coordinates.
More confident learners: Challenge these children to describe other 2D shapes using coordinates, including other quadrilaterals such as parallelograms and trapeziums.

Common misconceptions
Children cannot remember the order in which to give coordinates.
Methods to help children remember the order include **a** (across) comes alphabetically before **u** (up) and the *x* axis is a cross (across).

Probing questions
● How do you remember the order in which coordinates are written?
● Where else would we commonly find coordinates?

Next steps
Support: Set up situations in which children carry out coordinates work through games such as Battleships, using either commercially produced or homemade versions. Refer back to Year 5 Block D Unit 2.
Extension: Challenge children to draw a map of the school that includes their own coordinate reference system.

BLOCK D

Activities ⑨ and ⑩

Prior learning	**Framework objective**
Children can reflect, rotate and translate shapes on grids.	Visualise and draw on grids of different types where a shape will be after reflection, after translations, or after rotation through 90° and 180° about its centre or one of its vertices

Vocabulary
shape, grid, coordinates, position, direction, reflect, reflection, rotate, rotation, translate, translation, *x*-coordinate, *y*-coordinate, *x* axis, *y* axis, axes, quadrant

Resources
Interactive activities: Finding reflections, Finding rotations
Classroom resources: mirrors, tracing paper, card (for support)

⑨ Finding reflections

Introduce the interactive activity 'Finding reflections'. This activity offers a choice of reflection in the vertical axis, the horizontal axis or a diagonal line. Let the children use this activity to explore the reflections of a variety of shapes.

Teacher support
Less confident learners: Ask these children to start with simple shapes in a vertical or horizontal line.
More confident learners: Ask these children to reflect more complex shapes in a diagonal line and shapes one or two squares away from the mirror line.

Common misconceptions
Children complete a reflection of the shape they are working with but have difficulty locating it in its correct position.
Ensure that the children check that the reflected shape is identical to the original and that the distance of the shape from the mirror line stays the same.

Probing questions
● How do you know that the shape or pattern is reflected correctly?
● Where would the shape be after reflection?

Next steps
Support: Support with mirrors, tracing paper and card templates, when needed. Refer back to Year 5 Block D Unit 3.
Extension: Encourage children to move on to examples with two mirror lines. Refer also to the Year 6 extension or Year 7 material if appropriate.

⑩ Finding rotations

Introduce the interactive activity 'Finding rotations'. This activity offers a choice of rotation through 90° clockwise or anticlockwise or a rotation of 180°. Invite volunteers to come to the board to build the object and to predict where the image will be after it has been rotated.

Teacher support
Less confident learners: Start with a rectangle rather than a square as it is easier to see the rotation.
More confident learners: This activity also enables rotations of shapes that do not have a vertex or their centre as the centre of the rotation.

Common misconceptions
Children think that rotational symmetry may only be used to check the properties of shapes such as squares where the four equal sides and four equal angles can be found by folding or turning.
Show the children that rotational symmetry is useful for shapes such as the parallelogram, which has no bilateral symmetry. By turning the parallelogram, the opposite pairs of equal sides and the corresponding angles can be found.

Probing questions
● What does each small square look like after the rotation?
● Where would the image be if two rotations of 90° in the same direction were made consecutively?

Next steps
Support: Make sure that the children understand the concept of rotational symmetry by rotating basic shapes such as squares and checking that the pattern is the same. Refer back to Year 5 Block D Unit 3.
Extension: Ask children to investigate designs or company logos to find out how many times a tracing can be superimposed on the original through turning. Invite them to devise a rotationally symmetrical design for a new school badge. Refer also to the Year 6 extension or Year 7 material if appropriate.

BLOCK D

Unit 3 ⬜ Calculating, measuring and understanding shape

Introduction

This unit opens with opportunities to use and apply mathematics in practical problem-solving situations. It revisits mental methods and efficient written methods, methods of checking calculations, using decimal numbers, and working with both metric and imperial units. The unit concludes with work on perimeters and areas of compound shapes.

Framework objectives	Assessment focuses		Success criteria for Year 6	Learning outcomes
	Level 5	**Level 4**		
① Living costs				
Solve multi-step problems, and problems involving fractions, decimals and percentages; choose and use appropriate calculation strategies at each stage, including calculator use	• identify and obtain necessary information to carry through a task and solve mathematical problems, e.g. ● recognise information that is important to solving the problem, determine what is missing and develop lines of enquiry ● break a several-step problem or investigation into simpler steps ● consider efficient methods, relating problems to previous experiences	• develop own strategies for solving problems, e.g. ● make their own suggestions of ways to tackle a range of problems ● make connections to previous work ● pose and answer questions related to a problem ● check answers and ensure solutions make sense in the context of the problem ● review their work and approaches	• can use appropriate strategies when solving problems • can solve problems in real-life context situations • identifies and defines key words used when solving word problems • can find more than one strategy when solving problems	*I can solve problems with several steps and decide how to carry out the calculation.*
② Time out				
Calculate mentally with integers and decimals: U.t ± U.t, TU × U, TU ÷ U, U.t × U, U.t ÷ U	• use all four operations with decimals to two places, e.g. ● add and subtract numbers that do not have the same number of decimal places ● multiply or divide decimal numbers by a single digit, e.g. 31.62 × 7	• use a range of mental methods of computation with all operations, e.g. ● calculate complements to 1000 • recall multiplication facts up to 10 × 10 and quickly derive corresponding division facts, e.g. ● use their knowledge of tables and place value in calculations with multiples of 10 such as 30 × 7, 180 ÷ 3	• can add, subtract, multiply and divide whole numbers and decimals mentally • explains orally what mental methods have been used to find answers • can work against the clock as a way of speeding up mental calculations	*I can add, subtract, multiply and divide whole numbers and decimals in my head.*

BLOCK D

Unit 3 📖 Calculating, measuring and understanding shape

Framework objectives	Assessment focuses		Success criteria for Year 6	Learning outcomes
	Level 5	Level 4		
③ Decision time				
Use efficient written methods to add and subtract integers or decimals, to multiply and divide integers or decimals by a one-digit integer, and to multiply two-digit and three-digit integers by a two-digit integer	• understand and use an appropriate non-calculator method for solving problems that involve multiplying and dividing any three-digit number by any two-digit number	• use efficient written methods of addition and subtraction and of short multiplication and division, e.g. • calculate 1202 + 45 + 367 or 1025 – 336 • add and subtract decimals to two places • multiply a simple decimal by a single digit, e.g. • calculate 36.2 × 8	• knows when to use efficient written methods to do calculations • can explain to others the type of written methods chosen • shows evidence of being able to add, subtract, multiply and divide using efficient written methods	*I can add, subtract, multiply and divide whole numbers and decimals using efficient written methods.*
④ Find the key				
Use a calculator to solve problems involving multi-step calculations	• use a calculator where appropriate to calculate fractions/percentages of quantities/measurements, e.g. • find fractions of quantities such as 3/8 of 980 • find percentages such as 15% of 360g	• use inverse operations, e.g. • use a calculator and inverse operations to find missing numbers, including decimals • solve problems with or without a calculator	• knows when to use a calculator to work out calculations • can describe which keys were used to solve calculation problems • can demonstrate to others the method used on the calculator	*I can use a calculator to solve problems with several steps.*
⑤ Divisibility				
Use approximations, inverse operations and tests of divisibility to estimate and check results	• approximate to check answers to problems are of the correct magnitude • check solutions by applying inverse operations or estimating using approximations • check results, considering whether these are reasonable, e.g. • check as they work, spotting and correcting errors and reviewing methods	• check the reasonableness of results with reference to the context or size of numbers • develop own strategies for solving problems, e.g. • check answers and ensure solutions make sense in the context of the problem • review their work and approaches	• knows the main tests of divisibility • knows that different criteria have to be applied to numbers when finding tests of divisibility • check answers at the end of a calculation using an alternative method	*I can estimate the result of a calculation.* *I know several ways of checking answers.*
⑥ New measures				
Select and use standard metric units of measure and convert between units using decimals to two places (e.g. change 2.75 litres to 2750ml, or vice versa)	• solve problems involving the conversion of units, e.g. • solve problems such as 1.5kg ÷ 30g • work out approximately how many kilometres are equivalent to 20 miles	• choose and use appropriate units and instruments	• can convert one unit of metric measure to another using decimal numbers where appropriate • can work with some less familiar metric measures such as centilitres and tonnes	*I can convert a measurement in one unit to another using a related unit.* *I use decimals to do this.*

BLOCK D

Unit 3 ⬜ Calculating, measuring and understanding shape

Framework objectives	Assessment focuses		Success criteria for Year 6	Learning outcomes
	Level 5	Level 4		
⑦ All change (length)				
Solve problems by measuring, estimating and calculating; measure and calculate using imperial units still in everyday use; know their approximate metric values	• solve problems involving the conversion of units, e.g. ◦ work out approximately how many kilometres are equivalent to 20 miles • make sensible estimates of a range of measures in relation to everyday situations	There is no assessment focus for this level	• can identify and use selected imperial measures, especially inches and yards • knows the approximate metric values of chosen imperial measures • can appreciate situations in which imperial units might be used	*I know that 1 pint is just over half a litre, and that 1 litre is about 1¾ pints.* *I know that 1 mile is about 1.6km, and that 1km is about 5/8 of a mile.*
⑧ Make the rule				
Read and interpret scales on a range of measuring instruments, recognising that the measurement made is approximate and recording results to a required degree of accuracy; compare readings on different scales, for example when using different instruments	• read and interpret scales on a range of measuring instruments, explaining what each labelled division represents • measure and draw angles to the nearest degree, when constructing models and drawing or using shapes, e.g. ◦ measure and draw reflex angles to the nearest degree, when neither edge is horizontal/vertical	• interpret, with appropriate accuracy, numbers on a range of measuring instruments, e.g. ◦ measure a length using millimetres, to within 2mm ◦ measure and draw acute and obtuse angles to the nearest 5°, when one edge is horizontal/vertical	• is able to read scales on a variety of measuring instruments • can explain what each labelled division represents on a scale • can explain a scale when divisions are not labelled • can compare readings on different scales • can represent the same quantity on a range of different scales	*I can read scales as accurately as a problem requires.* *I can compare readings from different scales.*
⑨ Finding area ⑩ Area				
Calculate the perimeter and area of rectilinear shapes; estimate the area of an irregular shape by counting squares	• understand and use the formula for the area of a rectangle and distinguish area from perimeter, e.g. ◦ find the length of a rectangle given its perimeter and width ◦ find the area or perimeter of simple L shapes, given some edge lengths	• find perimeters of simple shapes and find areas by counting squares, e.g. ◦ use the terms 'area' and 'perimeter' accurately and consistently ◦ find areas by counting squares and part squares	• can define the word 'area' when applied to shapes • understands that area is concerned with the amount of surface covered • can use a calculation strategy to find area rather than counting squares • can find the area of compound shapes • can estimate the area of irregular shapes	*I can find the perimeter and area of shapes and estimate the area of irregular shapes.*

BLOCK D

| Activity ①

Framework objective
Solve multi-step problems and problems involving decimals; choose and use appropriate calculation strategies at each stage, including calculator use

Vocabulary
problem, solution, answer, method, strategy, operation, calculation, calculate, calculator

Resources
Worksheet: Living costs
Classroom resources: calculators

① Living costs

Provide the children with copies of the worksheet 'Living costs'. This activity asks them to solve a problem involving a monthly salary and the cost of essential items.

Teacher support
Less confident learners: It may be necessary to revise the methods used to find percentages before tackling the problem.
More confident learners: Encourage these children to explain how they obtained the solution using at least two different methods of working.

Common misconceptions
Children sometimes misinterpret key words or confuse operations, especially when they are working with percentages.
Spend time revising and discussing the meaning of key words. Revise how to use the percentage facility on a calculator.

Probing questions
● How many calculations were needed in order to solve the problem?
● Could written methods be used or was it necessary to use a calculator, particularly for the sections involving percentages?

Next steps
Support: Analyse the steps taken by children to solve the problem. Did one calculation follow on logically from another to obtain the solution? Refer back to Year 6 Block A Units 2 and 3.
Extension: Set more complex problems involving percentages – for example, topics such as VAT charges and building society interest rates. Refer also to Year 6 Block E Units 1 and 3.

BLOCK D

Activity ②

Prior learning
Children can add, subtract, multiply and divide whole numbers and decimals mentally.

Framework objective
Calculate mentally with integers and decimals: U.t ± U.t, TU × U, TU ÷ U, U.t × U, U.t ÷ U

Vocabulary
integer, decimal, decimal point, decimal place, add, subtract, multiply, divide, mentally, salary, percentage

Resources
Resource sheets: Time out, Self-assessment
Classroom resources: calculators, stopwatches

② Time out

Give the children a quick-fire test using the questions on the resource sheet 'Time out'. (Read the questions aloud or display the sheet on the board.) Let the children use stopwatches to time themselves. Ask them to work through the test using a calculator. Record how long they took and how many of their answers were correct. Then cover the answers. Do the test again, this time working mentally without a calculator, and record how long it took. Did they beat the calculator? How did the number of right answers compare? Decide whether to use the self-assessment sheet for the children to record their achievements and next steps.

Teacher support
Less confident learners: If necessary, set these children realistic time limits so that they have an attainable target to achieve.
More confident learners: Ask these children to devise their own set of timed questions that they can try out on their partners/friends.

Common misconceptions
Children have problems with decimal numbers when multiplying by 10 and 100. Encourage these children to use quick ways of working. When multiplying by 10 or 100, numbers move one or two places, respectively, to the left. When dividing by 10 or 100, numbers move one or two places, respectively, to the right. Reinforce that the decimal point does not move, only the digits.

Probing questions
● Tell me the best way of checking that your answers are correct.
● Can you suggest practical situations when having to work out calculations like this mentally is an advantage?

Next steps
Support: Suggest that the children work through the easier questions first and then return to those that cause them most difficulty. Refer back to Year 6 Block A Units 1, 2 and 3, Block D Units 1 and 2.
Extension: Invite children to work on speed test questions that contain three statements instead of two (for example, 0.5 + 0.2 + 0.7; 2 × 4 × 3; 10 − 2.5 − 1.5). Refer also to Year 6 Block E Units 1 and 3.

Activity ③

Prior learning
Children can add, subtract, multiply and divide whole numbers and decimals using efficient written methods.

Framework objective
Use efficient written methods to add and subtract integers and decimals, to multiply and divide integers and decimals by a one-digit integer and to multiply two-digit and three-digit integers by a two-digit integer

Vocabulary
calculate, calculation, operation, answer, method, strategy, jotting, explain, place value, digit, number, integer, decimal point, decimal place

Resources
Display page: Decision time
Resource sheet: Self-assessment

③ Decision time

First ask the children to provide you with examples of addition and subtraction problems involving decimals that (a) they would do in their head and (b) they would do on paper using an efficient written method. Encourage them to explain the reasons for their choice. Then reveal the problems on the display page 'Decision time' and ask the children to show you how they would find solutions to these problems using efficient written methods. When they have done this, decide whether to use the self-assessment sheet for the children to record their achievements and what they need to do next.

Teacher support
Less confident learners: Spend some time with these children discussing the best way to start the problems and the steps needed to find the solution.
More confident learners: Stress that when using a written method all aspects of the working out should be shown clearly and neatly.

Common misconceptions
Children believe that formal written methods are too long and complicated and that shortcuts can be used.
Convince these children that, in some cases, written methods are the only way of working to ensure that the correct solution is reached.

Probing questions
● What determines whether a calculation can be worked out mentally, using jottings or that a full written method should be used?
● Should efficient written methods also be used when the solution to a problem is being checked?

Next steps
Support: Discuss the strategy children have used to solve the problems and check particularly the positioning of any decimal points. Refer back to Year 6 Block A Units 2 and 3, Block D Units 1 and 2.
Extension: Encourage children to find problems where even written methods would prove difficult and the use of the calculator would be advised. Refer also to Year 6 Block E, Units 1 and 3.

BLOCK D

Activity ④

Prior learning
Children can use a calculator to solve problems with several steps.

Framework objective
Use a calculator to solve problems involving multi-step calculations

Vocabulary
problem, solution, calculate, calculation, operation, answer, method, strategy, explain, reason, calculator, function, key, display, enter, clear

Resources
Resource sheet: Self-assessment
Classroom resources: calculators

④ Find the key

Ask the children to use a calculator to solve this problem: *Steve is 1.4m tall. Anton is 95cm tall. Angela's height is exactly halfway between the heights of Steve and Anton. How tall is Angela?* (1m 17.5cm) Ask the children to list, ready for discussion, the calculator keys they pressed in order to solve the problem. Ask them to write down the calculations they did and to demonstrate how they used the calculator to find the answer. Decide whether to use the self-assessment sheet for the children to record their achievements and next steps.

Teacher support
Less confident learners: Ensure that these children are clear about the order in which the various parts of the problem have been answered.
More confident learners: Suggest that these children look for ways in which the puzzle can be solved using the least number of calculator keys.

Common misconceptions
Children try to feed too many operations into the calculator at the same time, forgetting the order in which different parts of the problem have to be calculated.
Stress that, where a number of operations/calculations have to be carried out, it may be necessary to jot some of them down on paper as a record.

Probing questions
● What calculations actually needed to be done in order to find the answer?
● Would it be possible to do the calculation with fewer keys pressed?

Next steps
Support: Spend time with children listening to their oral accounts of the keys they used to find the answer to the problem. Refer back to Year 6 Block A Units 1, 2 and 3, Block B Units 2 and 3, Block C Units 2 and 3.
Extension: Ask children to compare the time it takes to work out a problem like this on a calculator with the time taken to use usual written methods. *Which is quicker? Which is easier?* Refer also to Year 6 Block E Units 1, 2 and 3.

BLOCK D

Activity ⑤

Prior learning
Children can check answers in a number of different ways.

Framework objective
Use approximations, inverse operations and tests of divisibility to estimate and check results

Vocabulary
estimate, check, approximate, multiple, product, quotient, factor, multiply, divide, divisible, test of divisibility

Resources
Interactive activity: Divisibility

⑤ Divisibility

Show the children the interactive activity 'Divisibility'. Ask them to work their way through the questions and drag and drop the numbers into the appropriate boxes once they have tested their properties.

Teacher support
Less confident learners: These children may need some revision of the rules of testing the divisibility of numbers before they actually start.
More confident learners: Make sure that these children can write out the rules for divisibility by 3, 6 and 9 clearly and also describe others, such as the tests for divisibility by 2, 5 and 10.

Common misconceptions
Children assume that general rules about divisibility will cover a series of numbers – for example, if a number is divisible by 3 it will also be divisible by 6 and 9.
Point out that numbers such as 3, 6 and 9 are connected to each other as a number family but that different criteria have to be applied to each of them separately when it comes to tests of divisibility.

Probing questions
● When talking about multiplication and division facts, what do the terms *factor* and *multiple* mean?
● Sum up the rules for each of tests of divisibility in a short concise sentence.

Next steps
Support: Children will need a good knowledge of their multiplication tables up to 10 × 10 if they are to use tests of divisibility successfully. Refer back to Year 6 Block A Units 1, 2 and 3, Block B Units 1, 2 and 3.
Extension: Challenge children to find simple tests of divisibility by 4 and 8. Can they find a suitable test of divisibility by 7? Refer also to Year 6 Block E Units 1, 2 and 3.

BLOCK D

Activity ⑥

Prior learning
Children can convert a measurement in one unit to another using a related unit and use decimals to do this.

Framework objective
Select and use standard metric units of measure and convert between units using decimals to two places (for example, change 2.75 litres into 2750ml, or vice versa)

Vocabulary
estimate, convert, measure, change, units, gram (g), kilogram (kg), tonne (t), litre (l), millilitre (ml), centilitre (cl), millimetre (mm), centimetre (cm), metre (m), kilometre (km)

Resources
Worksheet: New measures

⑥ New measures

Give out the worksheet 'New measures'. In this activity, the children have to work with some of the less common metric measures, namely centilitres (capacity) and tonnes (mass). They will carry out conversions involving the use of decimal numbers.

Teacher support
Less confident learners: Ensure that these children realise before starting the task that 1 centilitre (cl) = 10ml or 0.01 litres and that there are 1000kg in a metric tonne.
More confident learners: Provide these children with practical capacity measuring tasks in the classroom where amounts have to be measured using centilitres.

Common misconceptions
Children confuse the word tonne (metric units) with ton (imperial units) which is still in use in Britain in some contexts.
Ensure that children appreciate that the metric tonne is 1000kg, while an imperial ton is equivalent to approximately 0.948 tonne.

Probing questions
● How many centilitres are equivalent to 1 litre?
● How many kilograms are equivalent to 1 metric tonne?

Next steps
Support: Despite conversions, stress that it is much easier to compare units by putting amounts into the same family. For example, 3500kg and 3.4 tonnes are more easily compared when expressed as either 3500kg and 3400kg or 3.5 tonnes and 3.4 tonnes. Refer also to Year 6 Block C Units 1, 2 and 3, Block D Units 1 and 2.
Extension: Encourage children to find examples of where the centilitre (bottles of wine) and the tonne (mass of cars, vans and so on) are used in real-life situations. Refer also to the Year 6 extension or Year 7 material if appropriate.

Activity ⑦

Prior learning
Children can name imperial measures still in everyday use and give their approximate metric equivalents (for example, 1 inch = 2.54cm).

Framework objective
Solve problems by measuring, estimating and calculating; measure and calculate using imperial units still in everyday use; know their approximate metric values

Vocabulary
metric units, imperial units, estimate, approximate, convert

Resources
Interactive activity: All change (length)

⑦ All change (length)

Introduce the interactive activity 'All change'. In this activity the children have to drag arrows to join matching items listed in metric and imperial units.

Teacher support
Less confident learners: Offer help with some of the multiplication aspects of the conversions, especially the location of the decimal place.
More confident learners: Encourage these children to carry out measurements and simple calculations using imperial units, particularly inches, feet and yards.

Common misconceptions
Children cannot see the value of learning about imperial units when metric units are in common use throughout Britain.
Assure the children that some items are often measured in imperial units in this country, particularly distance.

Probing questions
● Give some examples of where imperial units of length, height and distance are still used in the UK today. (For example, people's height, car's speed.)

Next steps
Support: Display conversion charts and facts about imperial units/metric units when children are working on these tasks. Refer back to Year 6 Block D Unit 1.
Extension: Make sure children are familiar with the conversion between miles and kilometres when working on problems involving long distances.

BLOCK D

Activity ⑧

Prior learning
Children can read scales as accurately as a problem requires. They can compare readings from different scales.

Framework objective
Read and interpret scales on a range of measuring instruments, recognising that the measurement made is approximate and recording results to a required degree of accuracy; compare readings on different scales, for example when using different instruments

Vocabulary
estimate, approximate, scale, division, interval, length, height, distance

Resources
Worksheet: Make the rule

⑧ Make the rule

Hand out copies of the worksheet 'Make the rule'. On this sheet the children are asked to mark, with arrows, the measurements given on different ruler scales. Explain that two rulers are marked in centimetres only and the other two just show millimetres.

Teacher support
Less confident learners: Make sure that these children are familiar with the conversion from millimetres to centimetres, and vice versa.
More confident learners: Ask: *How would you show the measurements given as decimals of a metre?*

Common misconceptions
Children believe that a measurement of length can only be written using one type of unit.
Emphasise that a measurement of length can be written in a number of different units but still remain the same distance (for example, 49mm is the same as 4cm 9mm and 4.9cm).

Probing questions
● How are millimetres converted into centimetres and vice versa?
● From what point on the ruler are accurate measurements made?

Next steps
Support: Point out to children that measurement cannot always be exact. Sometimes it is permissible to use the term 'about' or to give answers to the nearest unit. Refer also to Year 6 Block C Units 1, 2 and 3, Block D Unit 1.
Extension: When measuring small objects in the classroom, encourage children to give lengths in both millimetres and centimetres.

Activities ⑨ and ⑩

Prior learning Children can find the area of shapes and estimate the area of irregular shapes.	**Framework objective** Calculate the perimeter and area of rectilinear shapes; estimate the area of an irregular shape by counting squares

Vocabulary
measure, estimate, distance, length, height, width, perimeter, area, surface area, irregular, rectilinear, standard units, metric units, millimetres (mm), centimetres (cm), metres (m), square centimetres (cm²), square metres (m²)

Resources
Interactive activities: Finding area, Area (ITP)
Resource sheet: Self-assessment
Classroom resources: squared paper

⑨ Finding area

Introduce the interactive activity 'Finding area'. This activity challenges the children to find the area of rectangles without counting squares individually. Figures of various other shapes can also be formed using the small squares.

Teacher support
Less confident learners: Start with simple rectangles until children get used to calculating the area which can then be checked by counting the small squares.

More confident learners: Make up some non-rectangular shapes using the small squares and ask the children to investigate their areas.

Common misconceptions

Children consider area to be a measurement of distance and not of surface.
Clearly show that when discussing area, what is being measured is the amount of surface in the shape. Also make it clear that area will always be measured in square units, ie how many (centimetre) squares it would take to cover the surface.

Probing questions
● How can the area of these shapes be calculated without counting small squares?
● Explain why calculating the length multiplied by the width will provide the area of a rectangle.

Next steps
Support: Keep reminding children that area is measured in square units (for example, cm²), the amount of (centimetre) squares that it takes to cover the surface. Refer back to Year 6 Block D Unit 1.
Extension: Make sure that the children experience finding the combined area of rectilinear shapes that are a combination of several rectangles or a rectangle and a square. Refer also to the Year 6 extension or Year 7 material if appropriate.

⑩ Area

Display the ITP 'Area'. This activity examines the skills and strategies that the children use to find the area of a polygon or other irregular shape. Polygons can be created either by using the automated solid shape or by building them up with elastic bands. Once the shape has been created, ask the children to find its area. Decide whether to use the self-assessment sheet for the children to record their achievements and what they need to do next.

Teacher support
Less confident learners: Use automatic solid shapes to create polygons. Add one small triangle at a time to show how the area increases.
More confident learners: Create polygons with the elastic bands to make the task more challenging.

Common misconceptions
Children assume that when finding the area only the whole squares of an irregular shape should be considered.
Revise the strategy children should use, namely to count whole squares first, then pair up half squares to make whole ones, and then add the two groups together to find the total area.

Probing questions
● Is it possible to estimate the area of the shape before the counting of the squares starts?
● What would happen to any small pieces of squares that might be left over when the half squares have been added up?

Next steps
Support: If shapes are large, make sure some kind of tallying system is used to keep a record of the number of squares that have been counted. Refer back to Year 6 Block D Unit 1.
Extension: Using a large piece of squared paper and a suitable model, calculate the approximate body surface area of one of the children. Refer also to the Year 6 extension or Year 7 material if appropriate.

Periodic assessment

These activities can be used at any time during the teaching of this block to assess those children that you think have achieved the objective. A grid highlighting the related assessment focuses and expected learning outcomes for each activity can be found on the CD-ROM.

Written methods

Framework objective
Use efficient written methods to add and subtract integers and decimals, to multiply and divide integers or decimals by a one-digit integer and to multiply two-digit and three-digit integers by a two-digit integer

Learning outcome
● I can add, subtract, multiply and divide whole numbers and decimals using efficient written methods.

Provide each child with a copy of the worksheet 'Written methods (2)'. Ask the children to work out the solutions to the two questions, without a calculator, using two distinctly different methods. They should show all working out and then talk through the stages of what they have done.

Go the distance

Framework objective
Select and use standard metric units of measure and convert between units using decimals to two places (for example change 2.75 litres to 2750ml, and vice versa).

Learning outcome
● I can convert a measurement in one unit to another using a related unit. I use decimals to do this.

Hand out copies of the worksheet 'Go the distance' and ask the children to complete it. They should convert metric lengths, heights and distances to decimals before placing them in the correct numerical order.

Translations

Framework objective
Visualise and draw on grids of different types where a shape will be after translation through 90° or 180° about its centre or one of its vertices

Learning outcome
● I can reflect, rotate and translate shapes on grids.

Ask the children to carry out the shape translation activities on the worksheet 'Shape up'.

Name	Date

Go the distance

1. Place these lengths in order of size, smallest first:

      90mm   7cm 8mm   6.5cm   48mm   9.8cm   4cm 3mm

_____

_____

2. Place these heights in order of size, largest first:

      1.75m   106cm   1m 32cm   1m 58cm   141cm   1.09m

_____

_____

3. Place these distances in order, smallest first:

      4.75km   3900m   6km 200m   4km 86m   5.002km   8003m

_____

_____

How easy?

Red

Amber

Green

How do you think you have done?

_____

_____

Name

Date

Shape up

◼ For each translation shown below, describe the translation that has taken place from Shape A to Shape B.

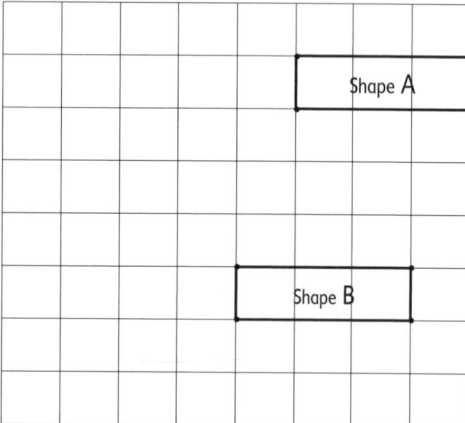

_____

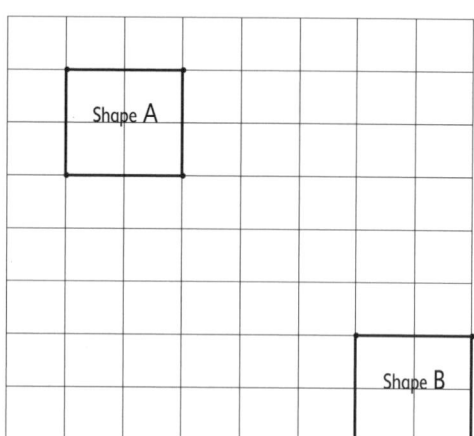

_____

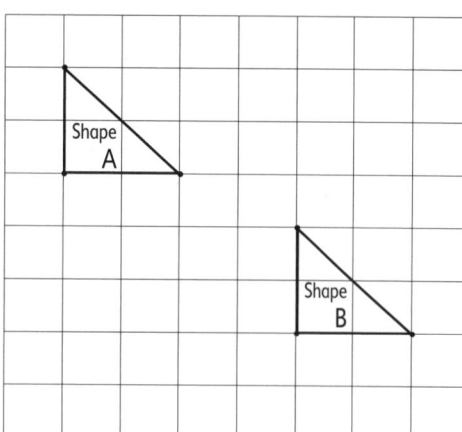

_____

How easy?

Red

Amber

Green

How do you think you have done?

_____

_____

BLOCK E
Securing number facts, relationships and calculating

Expected prior learning
Check that children can already:
- solve one- and two-step problems involving whole numbers and decimals
- use understanding of place value to multiply and divide whole numbers and decimals by 10, 100 or 1000
- use efficient written methods to add and subtract whole numbers and decimals with up to two decimal places, to multiply HTU × U and TU × TU, and to divide TU ÷ U
- find equivalent fractions
- understand percentage as the number of parts in every 100, and express tenths and hundredths as percentages
- use sequences to scale numbers up or down
- find simple fractions of percentages of quantities.

Objectives overview
The text in this diagram identifies the focus of mathematics learning within the block.

Key aspects of learning
- Problem solving
- Communication
- Reasoning

Solving multi-step problems with integers and decimals

Solving problems with fractions and percentages

Solving problems by tabulating systematically

Explaining reasoning

Recording solutions, using symbols where appropriate

Checking solutions in context

Simplifying fractions

Ordering fractions

Equivalent fractions, decimals, percentages

Fractions and percentages of quantities

**BLOCK E:
Securing number facts, relationships and calculating**

Mental methods with decimals

Written methods: HTU × TU, U.t × U, HTU ÷ U, U.t ÷ U

Using a calculator

Solving direct proportion problems by scaling numbers up and down

Unit 1 📖 Securing number facts, relationships and calculating

Introduction
This block of lessons secures children's understanding of number facts and relationships. Children are encouraged to think about how to solve problems systematically, and to record and explain their reasoning, as well as applying calculation strategies. Other lessons reinforce children's knowledge and use of number facts and secure their ability to use efficient written methods to calculate, and to apply relationships. They work with fractions, relating these to multiplication and division, and also scaling of numbers to solve direct proportion problems.

Framework objectives	Assessment focuses		Success criteria for Year 6	Learning outcomes
	Level 5	Level 4		
① Post it!				
Tabulate systematically the information in a problem or puzzle; identify and record the steps or calculations needed to solve it, using symbols where appropriate; interpret solutions in the original context and check their accuracy	● show understanding of situations by describing them mathematically using symbols, words and diagrams, e.g. ● organise their work from the outset, looking for ways to record systematically ● decide how best to represent conclusions, using appropriate recording ● begin to understand and use formulae and symbols to represent problems ● check results, considering whether these are reasonable, e.g. ● check as they work, spotting and correcting errors and reviewing methods	● present information and results in a clear and organised way, e.g. ● organise written work, e.g. record results in order ● begin to work in an organised way from the start ● consider appropriate units ● use related vocabulary accurately ● develop own strategies for solving problems, e.g. ● check answers and ensure solutions make sense in the context of the problem ● review their work and approaches	● is able to identify the key information ● is able to identify the steps and calculations that are needed for the task ● can decide on criteria for organising information ● records information systematically ● checks solutions	*I can record the calculations needed to solve a problem and check that my working is correct.*
② What to wear?				
Explain reasoning and conclusions, using words, symbols or diagrams as appropriate	● draw simple conclusions of their own and give an explanation of their reasoning, e.g. ● explain and justify their methods and solution ● identify more complex patterns, making generalisations in words and begin to express generalisations using symbolic notation ● use examples and counter-examples to justify conclusions	● search for a solution by trying out ideas of their own, e.g. ● check their methods and justify answers ● identify patterns as they work and form their own generalisations/rules in words	● is able to identify the task and the calculations required ● works out the different combinations ● is able to identify patterns ● articulates the process being followed ● justifies results and conclusions	*I can talk about how I solve problems.*

Unit 1 ◻ Securing number facts, relationships and calculating

Framework objectives	Assessment focuses		Success criteria for Year 6	Learning outcomes
	Level 5	Level 4		
③ Discount electrics				
Solve multi-step problems, and problems involving fractions, decimals and percentages; choose and use appropriate calculation strategies at each stage, including calculator use	● identify and obtain necessary information to carry through a task and solve mathematical problems, e.g. ● recognise information that is important to solving the problem, determine what is missing and develop lines of enquiry ● break a several-step problem or investigation into simpler steps ● consider efficient methods, relating problems to previous experiences	● develop own strategies for solving problems, e.g. ● make their own suggestions of ways to tackle a range of problems ● make connections to previous work ● pose and answer questions related to a problem ● check answers and ensure solutions make sense in the context of the problem ● review their work and approaches	● knows the meaning of key vocabulary used in problems ● identifies the critical information ● uses a coherent strategy for solving the problems ● is able to calculate percentages ● describes the strategy used to find the solution ● applies a strategy to check final results	*I can work out problems involving fractions, decimals and percentages using a range of methods.*
④ Which numbers?				
Use knowledge of place value and multiplication facts to 10 × 10 to derive related multiplication and division facts involving decimals (e.g. 0.8 × 7, 4.8 ÷ 6)	● use all four operations with decimals to two places, e.g. ● multiply or divide decimal numbers by a single digit, e.g. 31.62 × 7	● multiply a simple decimal by a single digit, e.g. ● calculate 36.2 × 8 ● quickly derive division facts that correspond to multiplication facts up to 10 × 10	● knows multiplication facts to 10 × 10 ● is able to identify relevant multiplication facts required ● can derive related decimal multiplication and division facts from these ● is able to position the decimal point accurately in the answer	*I can use place value and my tables to work out multiplication and division facts for decimals.*
⑤ Work it out				
Use efficient written methods to add or subtract integers or decimals, to multiply or divide integers or decimals by a one-digit integer, and to multiply two-digit or three-digit integers by a two-digit integer	● understand and use an appropriate non-calculator method for solving problems that involve multiplying and dividing any three-digit number by any two-digit number	● use efficient written methods of addition and subtraction and of short multiplication and division, e.g. ● calculate 1202 + 45 + 367 or 1025 − 336 ● add and subtract decimals to two places ● multiply a simple decimal by a single digit, e.g. ● calculate 36.2 × 8	● knows when it is necessary to use efficient written methods ● sets out calculations appropriately ● applies operations accurately ● positions the decimal point accurately ● checks calculations	*I can use efficient written methods to add, subtract, multiply and divide whole numbers and decimals.*

Unit 1 ▢ Securing number facts, relationships and calculating

Framework objectives	Assessment focuses		Success criteria for Year 6	Learning outcomes
	Level 5	Level 4		
⑥ Carpet tiles				
Use a calculator to solve problems involving multi-step calculations	• use a calculator where appropriate to calculate fractions/percentages of quantities/measurements, e.g. • find fractions of quantities such as 3/8 of 980 • find percentages such as 15% of 360g	• use inverse operations, e.g. • use a calculator and inverse operations to find missing numbers, including decimals • solve problems with or without a calculator	• knows when to use a calculator and identifies the calculations that need to be done • accurately inputs data into the calculator • uses calculator functions such as the memory button effectively • reads and interprets the display	*I can, when needed, use a calculator to solve problems.*
⑦ Ordering fractions				
Express a larger whole number as a fraction of a smaller one; simplify fractions by cancelling common factors; order a set of fractions by converting them to fractions with a common denominator	• reduce a fraction to its simplest form by cancelling common factors • order fractions and decimals, e.g. • order fractions with different denominators	• recognise approximate proportions of a whole and use simple fractions and percentages to describe these, e.g. • convert mixed numbers to improper fractions and vice versa	• converts a mixed number to an improper fraction • identifies common factors in the denominator and the numerator • divides denominator and numerator by the common factor • identifies equivalent fractions • compares and orders fractions	*I can write a large whole number as a fraction of a smaller one, simplify fractions and put them in order of size.*
⑧ Match the amounts				
Relate fractions to multiplication and division (e.g. 6 ÷ 2 = ½ of 6 = 6 × ½); express a quotient as a fraction or decimal (e.g. 67 ÷ 5 = 13.4 or 13 2/5); find fractions and percentages of whole-number quantities	• use a calculator where appropriate to calculate fractions/percentages of quantities/measurements, e.g. • find fractions of quantities such as 3/8 of 980 • find percentages such as 15% of 360g	• recognise approximate proportions of a whole and use simple fractions and percentages to describe these	• recognises how a quotient can be expressed as a fraction or a decimal • finds a unitary fraction of a whole-number quantity • finds fractions of whole numbers • finds 1% of a whole-number quantity • finds other percentages of whole-number quantities	*I can find fractions and percentages of whole numbers.*
⑨ Bulk bake				
Solve simple problems involving direct proportion by scaling quantities up or down	• understand simple ratio • solve simple problems involving ratio and direct proportion, e.g. • begin to use multiplication rather than trial and improvement to solve ratio problems	• begin to understand simple ratio	• understands and uses the vocabulary of ratio and proportion • identifies the relevant proportions and their relationships • applies scaling to each of the values • calculates values	*I can scale up or down to solve problems.*

BLOCK E

Activity ①

Prior learning
Children can calculate multiples of two-digit numbers. They know strategies to solve a problem systematically.

Framework objective
Tabulate systematically the information in a problem or puzzle; identify and record the steps or calculations needed to solve it, using symbols where appropriate; interpret solutions in the original context and check their accuracy

Vocabulary
problem, solution, method, strategy, explain, predict, reason, reasoning, pattern

Resources
Worksheet: Post it!

① Post it!

Provide each child with a copy of the worksheet 'Post it!'. Ask the children to think about how they could design a table in order to show their calculations.

Teacher support
Less confident learners: Encourage the children to think of the values that can be made using multiples of individual stamps and then to think about adding together values using different stamps.
More confident learners: Ask these children to see if they can continue their table up to values of £1.

Common misconceptions
Children may find it difficult to know where to start.
Encourage children to start by thinking about the values they can make using just 5p stamps, and then to try adding multiples of 16p and 23p. Remind them that they can use as many stamps as they wish and any combination of stamps.

Probing questions
● Can you see a pattern developing?
● What was the value that you could not make with the three stamps? (34p) Why not?
● Are there any other values that you can't make?

Next steps
Support: Provide further practice, starting with just two different values of stamps. See also Year 5 Block E Unit 3.
Extension: Encourage children to investigate other stamp values. Which three stamp values would be the most useful to have? See also Year 6 Block E Unit 2.

BLOCK E

Activity ②

Prior learning
Children can identify and explain the steps that they need to take to solve a problem.

Framework objective
Explain reasoning and conclusions, using words, symbols or diagrams as appropriate

Vocabulary
problem, strategy, explain, predict, reason, reasoning, pattern

Resources
Worksheet: What to wear?
Classroom resources: coloured counters (for support), coloured pens, flipchart, individual whiteboards and pens

② What to wear?

Introduce the worksheet 'What to wear?'. The teacher or teaching assistant should work with groups of four or five children, carrying out the assessment orally.

Teacher support
Less confident learners: These children could be given a set of coloured counters to demonstrate practically how the combinations could be made up.
More confident learners: Discuss different ways of recording the options. Could the children work out the solution without a chart?

Common misconceptions
Children do not find all the combinations.
Make sure that the children tackle the problem systematically. For example, in the chart all the options with a red hat are investigated first, followed by all the options with a yellow hat, then a green hat.

Probing questions
● Can you see a pattern developing?
● Why do you think Sara started her chart with red hats? Could she have started in a different way?
● Is it possible to work out the solution without a chart?

Next steps
Support: Start with just two outfits (or just two colours) and discuss how the problem could be practically investigated. Give children other practical activities involving simple permutations, such as colouring flags with two or three colours. See also Year 5 Block E Unit 2.
Extension: Add an extra outfit in a different colour, such as blue. Alternatively, add an extra item of clothing such as shoes. Encourage children to investigate other permutation activities and to discuss how a formula could be arrived at. See also Year 6 Block E Unit 2.

■ SCHOLASTIC

Activity

Prior learning
Children can solve one- and two-step problems involving whole numbers and decimals. They can use percentages and find simple percentages either with or without a calculator.

Framework objective
Solve multi-step problems, and problems involving fractions, decimals and percentages; choose and use appropriate calculation strategies at each stage, including calculator use

Vocabulary
problem, solution, calculate, calculation, operation, percentage, method, reduction, saving, sale price, change

Resources
Worksheet: Discount electrics
Classroom resources: calculators

③ Discount electrics

Provide each child with a copy of the worksheet 'Discount electrics'. They may need a calculator. The children have to work out the best buys by calculating a discount and then comparing prices of each item from each shop or both items from one shop. They can buy one item from one shop and the other from the other shop. They then have to calculate change and see how many DVDs they can buy with the remaining money.

Teacher support
Less confident learners: Encourage these children to approach the problem systematically. Give verbal support regarding the order of calculations.
More confident learners: Encourage these children to predict which will be the best options and to work out all the possible combinations of purchases.

Common misconceptions
Children don't identify the order of operations correctly.
Encourage the children to read the question carefully and to consider and solve each part of the problem.

Children think that they must buy all the items at the same store.
Remind these children that they need to find the cheapest option, which means they can buy items at different stores.

Probing questions
● In what order must you do the calculations?
● How can you calculate 30% without a calculator?
● What is the easiest way to work out how many DVDs you can buy?

Next steps
Support: Provide some further examples of two-step problems. See also Year 5 Block E Unit 3.
Extension: Ask the children to consider other discounts. For example: *After 30% discount, what if a further 10% discount is given if they buy two items? How does this affect the overall cost? How does this differ from 40% discount?* See also Year 6 Block E Unit 3.

Activity ④

Prior learning
Children know the tables to 10 × 10 and they can relate table facts to decimal numbers. They can multiply two decimal numbers and can divide using decimal numbers.

Framework objective
Use knowledge of place value and multiplication facts to 10 × 10 to derive related multiplication and division facts involving decimals (for example, 0.8 × 7, 4.8 ÷ 6)

Vocabulary
multiply, decimal, divide, number sentence, sum, total, product

Resources
Interactive activity: Which numbers?

④ Which numbers?

The children should work individually on the interactive activity 'Which numbers?'. In this activity they need to complete number sentences involving multiplication or division of decimals.

Teacher support
Less confident learners: These children should initially calculate their own number sentences using the given numbers. Check that they have the decimal points in the correct position.
More confident learners: Challenge these children to find how many alternative answers there are and ask them to talk about why there are alternatives.

Common misconceptions
Children choose an answer where the decimal place is in the wrong position. Remind children to approximate their answer first so that they can see if their chosen solution makes sense.

Probing questions
● Can you see a pattern developing?
● How has your knowledge of times tables helped you?
● What do you notice about the number of digits after the decimal point?

Next steps
Support: Encourage the children to take one of the decimal numbers and then multiply by the different integers until they can predict the answers. See also Year 5 Block E Unit 2.
Extension: Encourage the children to list all the possible number sentences using the given set of numbers and add further decimal numbers. See also Year 6 Block E Unit 3.

BLOCK E

■SCHOLASTIC

Activity ⑤

Prior learning
Children can use a range of strategies for addition, subtraction, multiplication and division. They have a good understanding of place value.

Framework objective
Use efficient written methods to add and subtract integers and decimals, to multiply and divide integers and decimals by a one-digit integer, and to multiply two-digit and three-digit integers by a two-digit integer

Vocabulary
add, decimal, integers, method, subtract, strategy

Resources
Worksheet: Work it out

⑤ Work it out

Provide each child with a copy of the worksheet 'Work it out'. Ask the children to show their full workings for each calculation.

Teacher support
Less confident learners: Remind these children of the different strategies that they can use for calculations.
More confident learners: Encourage these children to also show strategies for checking their answers.

Common misconceptions
Children do not set out the calculations correctly.
Remind children to make sure that the decimal points are vertically in line when adding or subtracting.

Probing questions
● What written methods did you use?
● How can you check your answers quickly?

Next steps
Support: Give children further practice with each of the different operations. See also Year 6 Block D Unit 1.
Extension: Ask children to show alternative methods for the calculations, and to identify reasons why different methods are better for particular calculations. See also Year 6 Block E Unit 3.

BLOCK E

Activity ⑥

Prior learning
Children can carry out simple operations on the calculator and know when data can be left in the calculator for a two-step problem. They know how to use the memory button correctly.

Framework objective
Use a calculator to solve problems involving multi-step calculations

Vocabulary
area, calculate, calculator, calculation, decimal, display, enter, clear, explain, memory, method, operation, problem, solution

Resources
Worksheet: Carpet tiles
Classroom resources: calculators, squared paper (for support)

⑥ Carpet tiles

Provide the children with the worksheet 'Carpet tiles' and a calculator. In this activity they are required to find the cost of carpeting a room and record the keys that they pressed for each calculation.

Teacher support
Less confident learners: Give these children squared paper to draw the room using a suitable scale such that one square represents 0.5m × 0.5m. They can then work out how many tiles are needed.
More confident learners: Invite these children to consider the individual cost of the tiles. How much would the carpet cost if the tiles could be bought individually?

Common misconceptions
Children try to enter too many operations into the calculator at the same time and forget to clear between operations.
Remind these children to clear the calculator between operations. It may help to write down the answers at each stage of the calculation so that they are reminded to use the = key.

Children misread the calculator display.
Remind these children to approximate first so that they can check if their answer 'looks right'.

Children do not cost 'complete boxes' of tiles.
Remind these children to read the question carefully and think about how many 'boxes' of tiles are needed.

Probing questions
- How did you work out the area of carpet needed?
- How did you work out how many tiles were needed?
- How many carpet tiles would be left over after the room is carpeted?

Next steps
Support: Give the children similar tasks and help them to list the order of calculations that they are doing on the calculator. See also Year 5 Block E Unit 2.
Extension: The children could calculate costs for carpeting the room if carpet was sold by the roll – give different carpet widths, such as 3m or 4m, and a cost per square metre which is the same as the carpet tiles. (The children should calculate this as £7 per metre.) See also Year 6 Block E Unit 2.

BLOCK E

Activity ⑦

Prior learning
Children can convert mixed numbers to improper fractions and vice versa; they can find equivalent fractions.

Framework objective
Express a larger whole number as a fraction of a smaller one (for example, recognise that 8 slices of a 5-slice pizza represents $^8/_5$ or $1^3/_5$ pizzas); simplify fractions by cancelling common factors; order a set of fractions by converting them to fractions with a common denominator

Vocabulary
decimal fraction, equivalent, denominator, fraction, numerator, order

Resources
Interactive activity: Ordering fractions

⑦ Ordering fractions

Display the interactive activity 'Ordering fractions'. In this activity the children are asked to order the fractions displayed on the screen by dragging and dropping them onto a number line.

Teacher support
Less confident learners: Encourage the children to find a common denominator and then convert each fraction to its equivalent with that denominator before ordering them.
More confident learners: Ask these children to add other fractions to the line in the correct positions.

Common misconceptions
Children do not always recognise the equivalent fractions.
Remind the children of equivalent fractions that they know (for example, $^2/_4 = ½$) and encourage them to think about the relationships between the two.

Children confuse the denominator and the numerator.
Before starting, remind these children of the meaning of the two terms.

Probing questions
● How did you decide what the common denominator is?
● What happens to the numerator when you change the denominator?

Next steps
Support: Give the children more practice at finding equivalent fractions and then ordering them. Refer back to Year 5 Block E Unit 2.
Extension: Encourage the children to order fractions where it is not easy to find a common denominator. See also Year 6 Block E Unit 2.

BLOCK E

Activity ⑧

Prior learning
Children can find fractions and percentages of amounts.

Framework objective
Relate fractions to multiplication and division (for example $6 ÷ 2 = \frac{1}{2}$ of $6 = 6 × \frac{1}{2}$); express a quotient as a fraction or decimal (for example, $67 ÷ 5 = 13.4$ or $13^{2}/_{5}$); find fractions and percentages of whole-number quantities (for example, $^{5}/_{8}$ of 96, 65% of £260)

Vocabulary
decimal fraction, denominator, equivalent, fraction, numerator, percentage, per cent (%), amount, solution

Resources
Interactive activity: Match the amounts

⑧ Match the amounts

Display the interactive activity 'Match the amounts'. In this activity children are asked to calculate percentages and fractions of amounts and match their answers with the solutions provided on the screen.

Teacher support
Less confident learners: Encourage these children to work out all the answers before they start to match them. (They may use a calculator if they wish.)
More confident learners: Encourage these children to calculate the amounts without using a calculator.

Common misconceptions
Children are sometimes confused about the place value of their answer.
Remind these children that percentage means 'parts per hundred', and that they need to approximate their answer first.

When using a fraction as an operator, children just calculate a unitary fraction and forget to multiply by the numerator.
Remind these children that, for example, $\frac{3}{4} = \frac{1}{4} + \frac{1}{4} + \frac{1}{4}$.

Probing questions
● Does your answer look right?
● If you know what 10% is, how could you work out 15%?

Next steps
Support: Give the children further practice at using simple percentages such as 10% and 50%. Discuss with them how to find 1% and then multiples of this. See also Year 5 Block E Unit 3.
Extension: Using the percentages and fractions in the exercise, ask children to find percentages and fractions of other amounts and quantities. See also Year 6 Block E Unit 2.

Activity ⑨

<table>
<tr><td>

Prior learning
Children can use fractions as operators.

</td><td>

Framework objective
Solve simple problems involving direct proportion by scaling quantities up or down

Vocabulary
ratio, proportion, scale up, scale down, round

Resources
Display page: Bulk bake
Resource sheet: Self-assessment

</td></tr>
</table>

⑨ Bulk bake

Reveal the display page 'Bulk bake' and go through the questions with the children. They are required to find the quantities of ingredients needed for different amounts of cakes. When they have completed this activity, decide whether to use the self-assessment sheet for the children to record their achievements and what they need to do next.

Teacher support
Less confident learners: Remind the children to work out the quantities for one bun before they try to work out the other amounts.
More confident learners: These children could investigate quantities for other numbers of buns.

Common misconceptions
Children do not first work out the quantities need for one bun.
Ensure that the children have read the question correctly and then discuss how no other quantities can be worked out if they don't first know the quantities needed for one bun.

Probing questions
● How did you calculate quantities needed for one bun?
● How did this help to find quantities needed for larger batches of buns?
● Were there occasions when you needed to 'round' your answers?

Next steps
Support: Give children further examples of simple scaling activities using recipes. Refer back to Year 5 Block E Unit 2.
Extension: Look at more complex recipes and scale these up and down. See also Year 6 Block E Unit 2.

BLOCK E

Unit 2 ▢ Securing number facts, relationships and calculating

Introduction
This unit mainly focuses upon reinforcing children's knowledge and understanding of fractions and percentages, and applying these effectively. The children also have to relate fractions to multiplying and dividing. They use and apply their mathematics and must think about how to solve problems systematically, recording and explaining their reasoning. Other lessons deal with ratio and proportion.

Framework objectives	Assessment focuses		Success criteria for Year 6	Learning outcomes
	Level 5	Level 4		
① Find the alien				
Tabulate systematically the information in a problem or puzzle; identify and record the steps or calculations needed to solve it, using symbols where appropriate; interpret solutions in the original context and check their accuracy	• show understanding of situations by describing them mathematically using symbols, words and diagrams, e.g. ● organise their work from the outset, looking for ways to record systematically ● decide how best to represent conclusions, using appropriate recording ● begin to understand and use formulae and symbols to represent problems • check results, considering whether these are reasonable	• present information and results in a clear and organised way, e.g. ● organise written work, e.g. record results in order ● begin to work in an organised way from the start ● consider appropriate units ● use related vocabulary accurately • develop own strategies for solving problems, e.g. ● check answers and ensure solutions make sense in the context of the problem ● review their work and approaches	• is able to identify the key information • is able to identify the steps and calculations needed for the task • can decide on criteria for organising information • records information systematically • checks solutions	*I can record the calculations needed to solve a problem and check that my working is correct.*
② Seaside bus fares				
Explain reasoning and conclusions, using words, symbols or diagrams as appropriate	• draw simple conclusions of their own and give an explanation of their reasoning	• search for a solution by trying out ideas of their own, e.g. ● check their methods and justify answers ● identify patterns as they work and form their own generalisations/rules in words	• is able to identify the task and the calculations required • articulates the process being followed • is able to justify results and conclusions	*I can talk about how I solve problems.*
③ Author's millions				
Use a calculator to solve problems involving multi-step calculations	• use a calculator where appropriate to calculate fractions/percentages of quantities/measurements, e.g. ● find fractions of quantities such as ³/₈ of 980 ● find percentages such as 15% of 360g	• use inverse operations, e.g. ● use a calculator and inverse operations to find missing numbers, including decimals • solve problems with or without a calculator	• knows when to use a calculator • is able to identify the calculations that need to be done • accurately inputs data into the calculator • reads and interprets the display	*I can work out problems involving fractions, decimals and percentages using a range of methods.*

BLOCK E

Unit 2 ⬜ Securing number facts, relationships and calculating

Framework objectives	Assessment focuses		Success criteria for Year 6	Learning outcomes
	Level 5	Level 4		
④ Fraction line-up				
Express a larger whole number as a fraction of a smaller one; simplify fractions by cancelling common factors; order a set of fractions by converting them to fractions with a common denominator	• reduce a fraction to its simplest form by cancelling common factors • order fractions and decimals, e.g. 　◦ order fractions with different denominators	• recognise approximate proportions of a whole and use simple fractions and percentages to describe these, e.g. 　◦ convert mixed numbers to improper fractions and vice versa	• knows how to convert a mixed number to an improper fraction • is able to identify common factors in the denominator and the numerator • can divide the denominator and the numerator by the common factor	*I can write a larger whole number as a fraction of a smaller one, simplify fractions and put them in order of size.*
⑤ Dinner arrangements ⑥ Fraction action				
Relate fractions to multiplication and division; express a quotient as a fraction or decimal; find fractions and percentages of whole-number quantities	• use a calculator where appropriate to calculate fractions/percentages of quantities/measurements, e.g. 　◦ find fractions of quantities such as $3/8$ of 980 　◦ find percentages such as 15% of 360g	• recognise approximate proportions of a whole and use simple fractions and percentages to describe these	• recognises how a quotient can be expressed as a fraction or decimal • finds a unitary fraction of a whole-number quantity • finds fractions of whole-numbers • finds 1% (and other percentages) of a whole-number quantity	*I can find fractions and percentages of whole numbers.*
⑦ Which order? ⑧ School travel plan				
Express one quantity as a percentage of another (e.g. express £400 as a percentage of £1000); find equivalent percentages, decimals and fractions	• use a calculator where appropriate to calculate fractions/percentages of quantities/measurements, e.g. 　◦ find percentages such as 15% of 360g • use equivalence between fractions • use known facts, place value and knowledge of operations to calculate, e.g. 　◦ calculate simple fractions or percentages of a number/quantity	• recognise approximate proportions of a whole and use simple fractions and percentages to describe these, e.g. 　◦ recognise simple equivalence between fractions, decimals and percentages, e.g. ½, ¼, $1/10$, ¾	• can find 1% of a quantity • can find other percentages of quantities • can divide one quantity by another • multiplies by 100 to find the percentage • identifies equivalent percentages and decimals	*I can work out a quantity as a percentage of another and find equivalent percentages, decimals and fractions.*
⑨ How many tiles?				
Solve simple problems involving direct proportion by scaling quantities up or down	• understand simple ratio • solve simple problems involving ratio and direct proportion, e.g. 　◦ begin to use multiplication rather than trial and improvement to solve ratio problems	• begin to understand simple ratio	• understands and uses the vocabulary of ratio and proportion • identifies the relevant proportions and their relationships to each other • applies scaling to each of the values • calculates values	*I can solve problems using ratio and proportion.*

BLOCK E

Activity ①

Prior learning
Children can identify x- and y-coordinates on a grid. They can identify the steps needed to solve a problem.

Framework objective
Tabulate systematically the information in a problem or puzzle; identify and record the steps or calculations needed to solve it, using symbols where appropriate; interpret solutions in the original context and check their accuracy

Vocabulary
problem, solution, method, strategy, explain, predict, reason, reasoning, angle, degree, direction, coordinates, origin, x-axis, y-axis

Resources
Interactive activity: Find the alien

① Find the alien

Show the children the interactive activity 'Find the alien'. Players explore a 5 × 5 grid in order to locate the point where an alien is hiding (the alien is randomly positioned in each game). The player needs to enter different sets of coordinates, each time receiving feedback as to how close the alien is on the grid. The aim is to find the alien in the smallest number of moves.

Teacher support
Less confident learners: Ask these children for the grid references for the points chosen early in the activity to ensure that they understand the numbering system for coordinates.
More confident learners: Encourage these children to identify possible strategies to find the alien in the smallest number of moves.

Common misconceptions
Children may initially make random guesses to identify the location.
Encourage the children to think systematically, to record their strategies and to improve them.

Probing questions
● Describe, for example, the top left-hand corner point using horizontal and vertical coordinates.
● Are there some moves that you could have missed out?
● Explain the best strategy that you have found.

Next steps
Support: Work through the activity with the children, supporting them with the selection of moves. See also Year 6 Block E Unit 1.
Extension: Invite the children to develop their own game on paper. They should challenge partners to find the alien, using clues similar to those given in the interactive activity. See also Year 6 Block E Unit 3.

BLOCK E

Activity ②

Prior learning
Children can identify the factors of a number. They can identify the steps needed to solve a problem.

Framework objective
Explain reasoning and conclusions, using words, symbols or diagrams as appropriate

Vocabulary
problem, solution, method, strategy, explain, predict, reason, reasoning, pattern

Resources
Resource sheet: Self-assessment

② Seaside bus fares

This activity should be done in small groups with the teacher or teaching assistant. Give the children the following information, either on a whiteboard or orally: *Mr King drives the 30-seater seaside resort bus to the beach. The fare is a fixed price, so all passengers pay the same amount. At the end of the journey Mr King checks the money he has collected in fares and finds he has £9.79. He also noticed that every one of the passengers paid him with the same seven coins, but there were no 20p coins. How many 2p coins did he have?* Say to the children: *Jim works out that there were 11 passengers on the bus. Explain how he decided this. How could you continue to solve this problem?* Ask the children to discuss this and to explain, firstly, how Jim was able to work out how many passengers there were. Then encourage the children to solve the problem by working out how many 2p coins he collected. Once they have completed this activity, decide whether to use the self-assessment sheet for the children to record their achievements and what they need to do next.

Teacher support
Less confident learners: Give these children further clues to help them to find the number of passengers. Suggest that they look for factors of 979. For the second part of the problem, suggest that they work out how much each passenger paid and the different coins that could make that amount.
More confident learners: Omit from the problem the information that 'Jim works out that there are 11 passengers on the bus.' Ask the children to explain how they will decide how many passengers there are.

Common misconceptions
Children try to divide £9.79 by 7 as they are told that the passengers each paid with seven coins.
Point out to the children that the coins can be of different values and that they must think about what coin values there are (1p, 2p, 5p, 10p, 20p, 50p and £1).

Children think that the seven coins must all be different.
Remind the children to read the information carefully, and point out that there may be more than one of any particular coin included in the seven coins.

Probing questions
● How much did each passenger pay? (89p)
● How could you make up that amount of money without using any 20p coins?
● Which seven coins make up that amount of money? (50p + 10p + 10p + 10p + 5p + 2p + 2p)

Next steps
Support: Give these children simple problems to solve, and ask them to explain and justify each step they use. Refer back to Year 6 Block A Unit 3.

BLOCK E

Extension: Ask the children to devise their own problems and explain how they can be solved, then swap problems with a partner, asking them to explain their strategies and solutions. Refer also to Year 6 Block E Unit 3.

Activity ③

Prior learning
Children can carry out simple operations on the calculator and know when data can be left in the calculator for a two-step problem. They know how to use the memory button correctly. They know how to work out time-related calculations.

Framework objective
Use a calculator to solve problems involving multi-step calculations

Vocabulary
calculate, calculator, calculation, decimal, display, enter, clear, explain, method, operation, predict, problem, reason, reasoning, solution, strategy

Resources
Worksheet: Author's millions
Classroom resources: calculators

③ Author's millions

Give each child a copy of the worksheet 'Author's millions' and a calculator. Ask the children to work independently to complete the activity. Encourage them to record the calculations that they have done on their calculators.

Teacher support
Less confident learners: Help these children to identify the different steps needed to solve the problem and to complete one step at a time. Encourage them to write down the steps, along with the order of their calculations.
More confident learners: Encourage these children to use the functions of the calculator so that they do not need to clear the display until the final answer.

Common misconceptions
Children do not identify the correct calculation.
Ensure that children read the question carefully and discuss what is needed.

Children do not clear the calculator correctly in between calculations.
Remind children to decide whether they are continuing to use the data in the calculator. If they are starting a new calculation, they should check that the display and memory are both cleared.

Probing questions
● How do you calculate the earnings per minute/per hour?

Next steps
Support: Give further opportunities for children to use a calculator for solving problems. Encourage them to record each step in order to ensure that they are clear about their approach. Refer back to Year 6 Block A Unit 1.
Extension: Ask the children to suggest other investigations involving large numbers for which they could use the calculator. (For example, how many days, hours or minutes have they been alive?) Refer also to Year 6 Block E Unit 3.

BLOCK E

Activity ④

Prior learning
Children can recognise equivalent fractions.

Framework objective
Express a larger whole number as a fraction of a smaller one (for example, recognise that 8 slices of a 5-slice pizza represents $^8/_5$ or $1\,^3/_5$ pizzas); simplify fractions by cancelling common factors; order a set of fractions by converting them to fractions with a common denominator

Vocabulary
equivalent, denominator, fraction, numerator, order

Resources
Resource sheets: Fraction wall (for support), Self-assessment
Classroom resources: fraction cards as follows: $^1/_{16}-^6/_{16}$, $^1/_8-^8/_8$, $^1/_4-^4/_4$, $^1/_2$, $^1/_{10}-^{10}/_{10}$, $^1/_5-^5/_5$, $^1/_{20}-^{20}/_{20}$

④ Fraction line-up

This practical activity should be carried out in groups with the teacher or teaching assistant. It could also be carried out as a whole-class activity. Give each child a fraction card (see Classroom resources above) and tell them to look carefully at their fraction and work out some fractions that are equivalent to it. Tell the children that you want them to arrange themselves in a line in order or their fractions. Repeat the activity with children being given different fraction cards. Finally, suggest to the children that they combine with another group and order their fractions accordingly. Decide whether to use the self-assessment sheet for the children to record their achievements and next steps.

Teacher support
Less confident learners: Give these children a copy of the resource sheet 'Fraction wall' for reference.
More confident learners: These children will be able to do the activity just using the cards. Give this group a wider range of fractions, which do not all have a common denominator.

Common misconceptions
Children sometimes forget that the bigger the denominator, the smaller the fraction.
Remind children to look at fractions that they are familiar with and compare them. For example, they know that a quarter is smaller than a half.

Probing questions
● Which fraction did you start with?
● Are there some fractions that are equal?

Next steps
Support: Give children more practical activities comparing fractions and then ordering them. Refer back to Year 6 Block E Unit 1.
Extension: Encourage children to extend this activity using a wider range of fractions. They may add their own fraction cards and then put them into the sequence. Refer also to Year 6 Block E Unit 3.

BLOCK E

Activities ⑤ and ⑥

Prior learning
Children can find simple fractions of quantities. They understand percentages as the number of parts in every 100 and can express tenths and hundredths as percentages.

Framework objective
Relate fractions to multiplication and division (for example, $6 ÷ 2 = ½$ of $6 = 6 × ½$); express a quotient as a fraction or decimal (for example, $67 ÷ 5 = 13.4$ or $13^2/_5$); find fractions and percentages of whole-number quantities (for example, $5/_8$ of 96, 65% of £260)

Vocabulary
decimal fraction, denominator, equivalent, fraction, numerator, percentage, per cent (%), quotient

Resources
Worksheets: Dinner arrangements, Fraction action

⑤ Dinner arrangements

Provide the children with copies of the worksheet 'Dinner arrangements'. Ask them to work through each question individually to find the correct fraction or percentage.

Teacher support
Less confident learners: Talk through the questions with the children. Remind them how to find percentages and fractions.
More confident learners: Ask these children to give all their answers as both percentages and fractions.

Common misconceptions
Children do not always give the answers that are asked for.
Remind the children to read the questions carefully and to identify what is being asked for.

Probing questions
● How did you work out your answers?
● For which questions is it easier to give the answer as a percentage and for which is it easier to give the answer as a fraction?
● How could you check your answers?

Next steps
Support: Give children more practice at finding simple percentages of whole numbers and then similar practice at finding fractions of whole numbers. Refer back to Year 6 Block E Unit 1.
Extension: Give children further opportunities to investigate finding percentages and fractions in real-life situations. Ask them to devise their own questions based on real-life situations. Refer also to Year 6 Block E Unit 3.

⑥ Fraction action

Give the children copies of the worksheet 'Fraction action'. Ask them to work through it individually to find the fractions and percentages of amounts.

Teacher support
Less confident learners: Remind these children how to find unitary fractions of whole-number quantities and to then multiply by the numerator.
More confident learners: Ask the children to find both the fractions and the percentages of each of the sets of quantities.

Common misconceptions
When children find fractions and percentages of quantities they confuse the units.
Remind these children to estimate their answers first and then to check that their answers make sense.

Probing questions
- How could you check that your answers are correct?
- How do you find $1/6$ of £63?
- How do you find 25% of 10kg?

Next steps
Support: Remind children how to find percentages using a calculator, and give them further practice at doing this. Refer back to Year 6 Block A Unit 1.
Extension: Ask children to devise their own questions finding percentages and fractions of quantities and to give them to their partners to try. Refer also to Year 6 Block E Unit 3.

Activities ⑦ and ⑧

Prior learning
Children can recognise equivalent fractions. They can order simple fractions. They can use a calculator to find a decimal equivalent of a fraction. They can understand percentages as the number of parts in every 100 and can express tenths and hundredths as percentages.

Framework objective
Express one quantity as a percentage of another (for example, express £400 as a percentage of £1000); find equivalent percentages, decimals and fractions

Vocabulary
decimal, equal, equivalent, explain, fraction, per cent (%), percentage, strategy, reason, reasoning, pattern

Resources
Interactive activity: Which order?
Worksheet: School travel plan
Classroom resources: calculators

⑦ Which order?

In the interactive activity 'Which order?', children are asked to order a set of fractions and match them with their decimal equivalents and also the related percentage. They need to select the required values at the foot of the screen and drag them into place on the table above.

Teacher support
Less confident learners: Encourage these children to look first at the values that they recognise (such as ½) and then compare them with other values to see if they are bigger or smaller. They may find it easiest to order the percentages first. Tell them that they may use a calculator to check their work.
More confident learners: Ask these children to copy the table onto paper and add extra values with their equivalents.

BLOCK E

Common misconceptions

Children do not recognise that fractions such as $1/3$ will give a recurring decimal.
Remind the children how to find the decimal equivalent of $1/3$, and make sure that they know that they must round this to two decimal places.

When ordering fractions, children look at the numerator and assume that if it is greater than 1 then it is bigger than other unitary fractions.
Remind children that, for example, $5/10$ is equivalent to ½, hence $4/10$ is less than ½.

Probing questions
- Which values did you order first? Why?
- What is the relationship between the decimal and the percentage?
- Which decimal values did you have to round?
- Which percentage values did you have to round?

Next steps
Support: Give children further practice at ordering simple fractions and finding decimal equivalents. For example, find all the decimal equivalents for $1/10$ to $10/10$. Repeat this with percentages and fractions such as eighths. Refer back to Year 5 Block E Unit 2.
Extension: These children may relate more complex values to decimals and percentages. Include sixteenths, twentieths, and so on. Refer also to Year 6 Block E Unit 3.

⑧ School travel plan

Provide each child with a copy of the worksheet 'School travel plan' and ask them to calculate the percentages based on the data given on the sheet.

Teacher support
Less confident learners: Read through the worksheet with these children and remind them how to find percentages. Help them to tackle one step at a time.
More confident learners: Encourage these children to explain how they found their answers. Ask: *Could you have used an alternative strategy?*

Common misconceptions
Children confuse the operation and use the numbers 'the wrong way around'.
Suggest that children refer to a percentage that they know (for example, 20 is 50% of 40), and think about the order of operation.

Probing questions
- Which percentage did you find first?
- How does it help to find 1%?
- How can you check your answer?

Next steps
Support: Give further practice at expressing one quantity as a percentage of another. Refer back to Year 6 Block A Unit 3.
Extension: Suggest that these children devise their own questions, initially related to the task and then changing the numbers. Refer also to Year 6 Block E Unit 3.

BLOCK E

Activity ⑨

Prior learning
Children can complete pattern sequences. They know the vocabulary related to ratio and proportion.

Framework objective
Solve simple problems involving direct proportion by scaling quantities up or down

Vocabulary
pattern, proportion, ratio, in every, for every, to every

Resources
Worksheet: How many tiles?
Classroom resources: coloured counters (for support)

⑨ How many tiles?

Provide each child with a copy of the worksheet 'How many tiles?'. The children are required to solve the ratio and proportion problems based on the tiles in the sequence. Tell them to show their workings in the space provided.

Teacher support
Less confident learners: Give these children coloured counters to support the activity practically.
More confident learners: Ask these children to predict how many of each tile would be needed for longer sequences and to suggest variations on the pattern.

Common misconceptions
Children do not identify the number of tiles in each section of the sequence. Remind children to check that the same tiles are repeated in the next section of the pattern.

Probing questions
● What colour would the next tile in the sequence be?
● What colour would the 25th tile be?
● How many more red tiles than white tiles would you need for a pattern of 40 tiles?

Next steps
Support: Give further practical examples for children to investigate. Revisit the language of ratio and proportion. Refer back to Year 6 Block E Unit 1.
Extension: Ask children to devise their own patterns using more than three colours and then write their own proportion sentences related to them. Refer also to Year 6 Block E Unit 3.

BLOCK E

Unit 3 Securing number facts, relationships and calculating

Introduction
This block of lessons revisits all of the objectives from Units 2 and 3. Some lessons reinforce the children's knowledge and use of number facts and their ability to use and apply these effectively, as well as securing their ability to use efficient methods of calculation. There is a strong emphasis on fractions and percentages, and applying these to problem solving. The relationship between fractions and multiplication and division is further explored.

Framework objectives	Assessment focuses		Success criteria for Year 6	Learning outcomes
	Level 5	Level 4		
(1) Triangular puzzles				
Tabulate systematically the information in a problem or puzzle; identify and record the steps or calculations needed to solve it, using symbols where appropriate; interpret solutions in the original context and check their accuracy	• show understanding of situations by describing them mathematically using symbols, words and diagrams, e.g. • organise their work from the outset, looking for ways to record systematically • decide how best to represent conclusions, using appropriate recording • begin to understand and use formulae and symbols to represent problems • check results, considering whether these are reasonable, e.g. • check as they work, spotting and correcting errors and reviewing methods	• present information and results in a clear and organised way, e.g. • organise written work, e.g. record results in order • begin to work in an organised way from the start • consider appropriate units • use related vocabulary accurately • develop own strategies for solving problems, e.g. • check answers and ensure solutions make sense in the context of the problem • review their work and approaches	• is able to identify the key information • is able to identify the steps and calculations needed for the task • can decide on criteria for organising information • uses symbols if appropriate • records information systematically • checks solutions	*I can record the calculations needed to solve a problem and check that my working is correct.*
(2) Day trip				
Solve multi-step problems, and problems involving fractions, decimals and percentages; choose and use appropriate calculation strategies at each stage, including calculator use	• identify and obtain necessary information to carry through a task and solve mathematical problems, e.g. • recognise information that is important to solving the problem, determine what is missing and develop lines of enquiry • break a several-step problem or investigation into simpler steps • consider efficient methods, relating problems to previous experiences	• develop own strategies for solving problems, e.g. • make their own suggestions of ways to tackle a range of problems • make connections to previous work • pose and answer questions related to a problem • check answers and ensure solutions make sense in the context of the problem • review their work and approaches	• knows the meaning of key vocabulary used in problems • uses a coherent strategy for solving word problems • describes the strategy used to find the solution • applies a strategy to check final results	*I can work out problems involving fractions, decimals and percentages using a range of methods.*

BLOCK E

Unit 3 ▢ Securing number facts, relationships and calculating

Framework objectives	Assessment focuses		Success criteria for Year 6	Learning outcomes
	Level 5	Level 4		
③ Decimal trios ④ Decimal puzzles				
Use knowledge of place value and multiplication facts to 10 × 10 to derive related multiplication and division facts involving decimals (e.g. 0.8 × 7, 4.8 ÷ 6)	● use all four operations with decimals to two places, e.g. ● multiply or divide decimal numbers by a single digit, e.g. 31.62 × 7	● multiply a simple decimal by a single digit, e.g. ● calculate 36.2 × 8 ● quickly derive division facts that correspond to multiplication facts up to 10 × 10	● knows multiplication facts to 10 × 10 ● is able to identify relevant multiplication facts required ● can derive related decimal multiplication and division facts from these	*I can use place value and my tables to work out multiplication and division facts.*
⑤ Sunflowers ⑥ Digit drop				
Use efficient written methods to add and subtract integers and decimals, to multiply and divide integers and decimals by a one-digit integer, and to multiply two-digit and three-digit integers by a two-digit integer	● understand and use an appropriate non-calculator method for solving problems that involve multiplying or dividing any three-digit number by any two-digit number	● use efficient written methods of addition and subtraction and of short multiplication and division, e.g. ● calculate 1202 + 45 + 367 or 1025 – 336 ● add and subtract decimals to two places ● multiply a simple decimal by a single digit, e.g. ● calculate 36.2 × 8	● knows when it is necessary to use efficient written methods ● sets out calculations appropriately ● applies operations accurately ● positions the decimal point accurately	*I can use standard written methods to add, subtract, multiply and divide whole numbers and decimals.*
⑦ Calculator quiz				
Use a calculator to solve problems involving multi-step calculations	● use a calculator where appropriate to calculate fractions/percentages of quantities/measurements, e.g. ● find fractions of quantities such as 3/8 of 980 ● find percentages such as 15% of 360g	● use inverse operations, e.g. ● use a calculator and inverse operations to find missing numbers, including decimals ● solve problems with or without a calculator	● knows when to use a calculator to work out a calculation ● is able to identify the calculations that need to be done ● accurately inputs data into the calculator ● reads and interprets the display	*I can work out problems involving fractions, decimals and percentages using a calculator.*
⑧ Fraction parts				
Express a larger whole number as a fraction of a smaller one; simplify fractions by cancelling common factors; order a set of fractions by converting them to fractions with a common denominator	● reduce a fraction to its simplest form by cancelling common factors ● order fractions and decimals, e.g. ● order fractions with different denominators	● recognise approximate proportions of a whole and use simple fractions and percentages to describe these, e.g. ● convert mixed numbers to improper fractions and vice versa	● knows how to convert a mixed number to an improper fraction ● is able to identify common factors in the denominator and the numerator ● is able to simplify fractions by dividing the denominator and the numerator by the common factor	*I can write a large whole number as a fraction of a smaller one and simplify fractions and put them in order of size.*

BLOCK E

Unit 3 ▢ Securing number facts, relationships and calculating

Framework objectives	Assessment focuses		Success criteria for Year 6	Learning outcomes
	Level 5	Level 4		
⑨ New curtains				
Relate fractions to multiplication and division (for example 6 ÷ 2 = ½ of 6 = 6 × ½); express a quotient as a fraction or decimal (for example 67 ÷ 5 = 13.4 or 13²/₅); find fractions and percentages of whole-number quantities (for example, ⁵/₈ of 96, 65% of £260)	● use a calculator where appropriate to calculate fractions/percentages of quantities/measurements, e.g. ● find fractions of quantities such as ³/₈ of 980 ● find percentages such as 15% of 360g	● recognise approximate proportions of a whole and use simple fractions and percentages to describe these	● recognises how a quotient can be expressed as a fraction or decimal ● is able to find a unitary fraction of a whole-number quantity ● is able to find fractions of whole-number quantities ● is able to find 1% of a whole-number quantity ● is able to find other percentages of whole-number quantities	*I can find fractions and percentages of whole numbers.*
⑩ Which group?				
Express one quantity as a percentage of another (for example, express £400 as a percentage of £1000); find equivalent percentages, decimals and fractions	● use a calculator where appropriate to calculate fractions/percentages of quantities/measurements, e.g. ● find percentages such as 15% of 360g ● use equivalence between fractions, e.g. ● convert fractions such as ²/₅ into tenths or hundredths and express them as decimals or percentages and vice versa ● use known facts, place value and knowledge of operations to calculate, e.g. ● calculate simple fractions or percentages of a number/ quantity, e.g. ³/₈ of 400g or 60% of £300	● recognise approximate proportions of a whole and use simple fractions and percentages to describe these, e.g. ● recognise simple equivalence between fractions, decimals and percentages, eg decimal and percentage equivalents of ½, ¼, ¹/₁₀, ¾	● knows how to find 1% of a quantity ● knows how to find other percentages of quantities ● is able to divide one quantity by another ● is able to multiply by 100 to find the percentage ● is able to identify equivalent percentages and decimals	*I can work out a quantity as a percentage of another and find equivalent percentages, decimals and fractions.*
⑪ Scale up				
Solve simple problems involving direct proportion by scaling quantities up or down	● understand simple ratio ● solve simple problems involving ratio and direct proportion, e.g. ● begin to use multiplication rather than trial and improvement to solve ratio problems	● begin to understand simple ratio	● is able to identify the relevant proportions and their relationships to each other ● can apply scaling to each of the values ● calculates values	*I can solve problems using ratio and proportion.*

■SCHOLASTIC

BLOCK E

Activity ①

Prior learning
Children can record their mathematical thinking in a variety of ways. They can explain their approach to an investigation.

Framework objective
Tabulate systematically the information in a problem or puzzle; identify and record the steps or calculations needed to solve it, using symbols where appropriate; interpret solutions in the original context and check their accuracy

Vocabulary
problem, solution, method, strategy, explain, predict, reason, reasoning, pattern

Resources
Resource sheets: Digit cards 1–9, Self-assessment

① Triangular puzzles

This activity should be carried out in small groups with a teacher or teaching assistant. Give each group a set of 1–9 digit cards. (The resource sheet 'Digit cards 1–9' can be used for this purpose.) Explain that you want the children to arrange the cards in a triangle, with four cards on each side. The task is to arrange the cards in such a way that the sum of the digits on each side is the same. Ask the children how they could tabulate the different arrangements. Decide whether to use the self-assessment sheet for the children to record their achievements and what they need to do next.

Teacher support
Less confident learners: Give these children just six digit cards, numbered 1–6, and ask them to create a triangle with three numbers on each side. When they have tabulated their answers, ask them to think about how the extra cards could be included.
More confident learners: Invite these children to find the arrangements that give the highest and lowest totals.

Common misconceptions
Children initially just place the numbers randomly into the triangle.
Encourage the children to think about the strategy they are going to use and, if necessary, to tabulate all the possible combinations.

Probing questions
● How did you decide which would be the numbers at the vertices of the triangle?
● How did it help to find all the possible totals?
● Have you found a pattern?

Next steps
Support: Give children other simple number puzzles and ask them to look at all the possibilities and record them. Refer back to Year 6 Block E Unit 1.
Extension: Encourage these children to look at more complex number puzzles (including 'magic squares') and to show diagrammatically how different solutions can be found. Refer also to the Year 6 extension or Year 7 material if appropriate.

BLOCK E

Activity

Prior learning
Children can calculate simple percentages. They can identify the steps needed to solve a problem.

Framework objective
Solve multi-step problems, and problems involving fractions, decimals and percentages; choose and use appropriate calculation strategies at each stage, including calculator use

Vocabulary
calculate, calculation, calculator, decimal, discount, method, percentage, problem, solution, strategy

Resources
Worksheet: Day trip
Resource sheet: Five steps to successful problem solving (for support)
Classroom resources: calculators

② Day trip

Give each child a copy of the worksheet 'Day trip'. Ask them to work through the problem, answering each question using the information that they are given.

Teacher support
Less confident learners: Read the problem through with these children and encourage them to identify the calculations that are required at each step. Decide on the best strategy to use for each calculation.
More confident learners: Ask these children to check their calculations using alternative methods. Encourage them to record how they have checked their answers.

Common misconceptions
Children work out the wrong percentages because they have not identified the required calculation correctly.
Ensure that the children read the problem carefully, noting the key information, and that they identify the steps and calculations required to solve each step of the problem.

Probing questions
● How did you calculate the discount?
● How could you check that your answer is correct?
● What is the easiest way to find 12½%?

Next steps
Support: Provide children with copies of the resource sheet 'Five steps to successful problem solving' and give further problems using the 'five steps' for support. Refer back to Year 6 Block D Unit 1.
Extension: Ask children to devise and solve their own 'day trip' problems, including discounts. These can be given to partners to solve. Refer also to the Year 6 extension or Year 7 material if appropriate.

BLOCK E

■■SCHOLASTIC

Activities ③ and ④

Prior learning
Children know multiplication facts up to 10 × 10. They are able to relate multiplication facts to decimals.

Framework objective
Use knowledge of place value and multiplication facts to 10 × 10 to derive related multiplication and division facts involving decimals (for example, 0.8 × 7, 4.8 ÷ 6)

Vocabulary
decimal, decimal fraction, decimal place, decimal point, divide, division, multiplication, multiply

Resources
Worksheet: Decimal puzzles
Resource sheets: Digit and symbol cards, Self-assessment
Classroom resources: multiplication squares (for support), stopwatches

③ Decimal trios

Play the 'Decimal trios' game. Ask the children to work in pairs. Each pair will need two or three sets of digit cards. (The resource sheet 'Digit and symbol cards' can be used for this purpose.) The digit cards should be shuffled and placed in a pile face down. Each child must take three digit cards, as well as a decimal point card and the × and ÷ cards. They should each then make a calculation including all of their digit cards, the decimal point and either the × or the ÷ card. For example: 0.6 × 8; 3 × 1.4; 2.8 ÷ 7. Ask the children to record their calculation and its answer and then give it to their partner to calculate. Repeat several times. Decide whether to use the self-assessment sheet for the children to record their achievements and what they need to do next.

Teacher support
Less confident learners: Give these children multiplication squares to refer to in order to check their times-table knowledge.
More confident learners: How many different calculations can the children make with the same three or four digit cards?

Common misconceptions
Children are unsure about where to put the decimal point.
Remind children to look carefully to see if their answer makes sense. Remind them of the rule about counting the number of digits after the decimal point.

Probing questions
● If you multiply two decimal numbers that are both less than 1, what do you know about the size of the answer?
● If you have a 0 after the decimal point, what do you have to remember?
● What is 0.5 times 0.5?

Next steps
Support: Give children further examples of working with multiplying or dividing decimal numbers with no more than three digits. As they work them out, ask them to estimate what their answers will be and then discuss with them any discrepancies. Refer back to Year 6 Block A Unit 1.
Extension: Give these children further practice with larger numbers. They could play 'Decimal trios' with more digit cards. Refer also to the Year 6 extension or Year 7 material if appropriate.

BLOCK E

④ Decimal puzzles

Give each child the worksheet 'Decimal puzzles'. Ask them to time themselves to see how quickly they can complete the activity.

Teacher support
Less confident learners: Give these children a multiplication square to refer to in order to check their times-table knowledge. Encourage them to think about accuracy rather than speed.
More confident learners: Set a time limit for children to complete the task.

Common misconceptions
Children are surprised that multiplying can give a smaller answer.
Explain that when multiplying by a fraction you are saying, for example, '½ of' rather than '½ times'.

Probing questions
● What is ³/₅ of 20?
● How could you express ³/₅ as a decimal?
● If you divide a number by 0.8, will the answer be bigger or smaller than the starting number? Explain why.

Next steps
Support: Give children practice at writing as many number sentences as they can from a multiplication fact involving a decimal number. Refer back to Year 6 Block E Unit 1.
Extension: Invite children to devise their own decimal puzzles involving multiplication facts, decimals and fractions, and ask their partners to solve them.

Activities ⑤ and ⑥

Prior learning
Children can apply at least one written method to add or subtract integers and decimals. They are able to use written methods for both multiplication and division.

Framework objective
Use efficient written methods to add and subtract integers and decimals, to multiply and divide integers and decimals by a one-digit integer, and to multiply two-digit and three-digit integers by a two-digit integer

Vocabulary
add, decimal place, decimal point, difference, divide, divisor, minus, multiple, multiply, plus, product, quotient, remainder, subtract, sum, total

Resources
Interactive activity: Digit drop
Display page: Multiplication methods (for support)
Worksheet: Sunflowers

⑤ Sunflowers

Provide each child with a copy of the worksheet 'Sunflowers'. Ask the children to solve each problem and record their written method at each step.

Teacher support
Less confident learners: Use the display page 'Multiplication methods' to remind these children about different written multiplication methods.
More confident learners: Encourage these children to show how they can check their answers using different methods and strategies.

Common misconceptions

Children make mistakes with place value.
When they are adding decimals, remind the children to make sure that the decimal points are in line and all the digits are in the correct columns. When multiplying and dividing, remind them to approximate first to ensure that their answers make sense.

Probing questions

- Explain how you found your answer.
- How do you know if your answer is correct?

Next steps

Support: Remind these children that when they are working with money they are carrying out decimal calculations. Give them further examples that they can relate to their own real-life experiences using money. Refer back to Year 6 Block A Unit 3.

Extension: Encourage these children to devise their own real-life problems and ask their partners to solve them. They should also show how they can check their work. Refer also to the Year 6 extension or Year 7 material if appropriate.

⑥ Digit drop

Ask the children to complete the interactive activity 'Digit drop' individually. Encourage them to work out the calculations first in their exercise books, showing the method that they have used, and then input their answers on the computer screen to check.

Teacher support

Less confident learners: Remind these children of the different methods that they can use to calculate the answers. Ask them to decide which is the best method for each calculation.

More confident learners: Encourage these children to use an alternative method to check their answers.

Common misconceptions

When children are writing out calculations, they put digits in the wrong column and consequently do not add up to get the correct answer.
Remind children about the importance of place value, and ask them to think about which column each digit should be in. Remind them to position their numbers carefully.

Probing questions

- Where did you start with this calculation?
- How could you check if your answer is correct?
- What did you estimate your answer would be?

Next steps

Support: Give children further practice at identifying a particular method, such as grid multiplication, to ensure that they are secure with at least one method of calculation. Refer back to Year 6 Block A Unit 3.

Extension: Encourage these children to think of practical applications for these calculations and to devise their own questions and problems. Refer also to the Year 6 extension or Year 7 material if appropriate.

BLOCK E

Activity ⑦

Prior learning
Children can carry out simple calculations using a calculator. They can accurately interpret the display on a calculator and relate it to the context of the calculation.

Framework objective
Use a calculator to solve problems involving multi-step calculations

Vocabulary
calculate, calculator, calculation, decimal, display, enter, clear, explain, method, operation, predict, problem, reason, reasoning, solution, strategy

Resources
Resource sheets: Calculator quiz, Self-assessment
Classroom resources: calculators

⑦ Calculator quiz

This practical activity should be done in small groups, with the teacher or teaching assistant, using the resource sheet 'Calculator quiz'. Read out each question and ask the children to follow the instructions. Tell them that you want them to listen to the calculation in full before starting to enter data; you will then repeat the calculation. After each stage, children should show their calculator display to ensure that it is correct and say what the display means. For questions 5–7, write the calculation with the missing digits on a whiteboard. Once the children have completed this activity, decide whether to use the self-assessment sheet so that they can record their achievements and what they need to do next.

Teacher support
Less confident learners: After each calculation, check the answer with these children to clear any confusion and, if necessary, give a second similar calculation.
More confident learners: Invite these children to suggest other calculations that could be done on the calculator, that would be much more difficult if using a written method.

Common misconceptions
Children do not clear the calculator correctly.
Ensure that these children know to check that the calculator is fully cleared before starting a new calculation.

When entering data on a calculator, children confuse the units (for example, when adding £1.20 and 95p they may enter 1.20 + 95).
Remind the children to ensure that the units are the same in all the amounts they are inputting – for example, £1.20 + £0.95 or 120p + 95p.

Probing questions
● Which keys did you press for this calculation?
● How can you check your answer?
● How did you decide where to start with your calculation?

Next steps
Support: Revise the use of inverse operations and encourage children to use this strategy when checking their calculations on the calculator. Refer back to Year 6 Block A Unit 1.
Extension: Give the children further multi-step calculations and ask them to devise some problems that can be done on the calculator, with more than two steps. Refer also to the Year 6 extension or Year 7 material if appropriate.

BLOCK E

Activity ⑧

Prior learning
Children can recognise improper fractions and can relate them to mixed fractions.

Framework objective
Express a larger whole number as a fraction of a smaller one (for example, recognise that 8 slices of a 5-slice pizza represents $8/5$ or $1\,3/5$ pizzas); simplify fractions by cancelling common factors; order a set of fractions by converting them to fractions with a common denominator

Vocabulary
cancel, decimal fraction, denominator, equivalent, fraction, improper fraction, mixed number, numerator, proper fraction, unit fraction

Resources
Worksheet: Fraction parts

⑧ Fraction parts

Hand out copies of the worksheet 'Fraction parts'. Ask the children to work through it independently to solve the fraction problems involving mixed numbers.

Teacher support
Less confident learners: Provide these children with practical fraction apparatus to work with in order to secure their understanding of fractions and mixed numbers.
More confident learners: Encourage these children to think of all the possible ways to express their answers.

Common misconceptions
Children find it difficult to understand the concept of mixed numbers and how they relate to improper fractions.
Remind children how to change mixed numbers to improper fractions and vice versa.

Probing questions
● How many sixths are there in $1\,1/2$? (9)
● How would you write that as an improper fraction? ($9/6$ or $3/2$)

Next steps
Support: Give further practice at converting mixed numbers into improper fractions and vice versa, relating this to real-life applications relevant to the children. Refer back to Year 6 Block E Unit 1.
Extension: Ask these children to think of real-life situations where we might use mixed numbers or where we need to express a large whole number as a fraction of a smaller one. Refer also to the Year 6 extension or Year 7 material if appropriate.

BLOCK E

Activity ⑨

Prior learning
Children can carry out division calculations that have a remainder. They can recognise the relationship between decimals and fractions.

Framework objective
Relate fractions to multiplication and division (for example, 6 ÷ 2 = ½ of 6 = 6 × ½); express a quotient as a fraction or decimal (for example, 67 ÷ 5 = 13.4 or 13²/₅); find fractions and percentages of whole-number quantities (for example, ⁵/₈ of 96, 65% of £260)

Vocabulary
decimal, decimal point, denominator, divide, fraction, mixed number, numerator, quotient

Resources
Worksheet: New curtains

⑨ New curtains

Give each child a copy of the worksheet 'New curtains'. Ask them to work through it independently, giving each answer as a fraction and as a decimal.

Teacher support
Less confident learners: Read through the problem with these children and encourage them to think about what the question means. Remind them that they are 'sharing' and that they must also 'share' the remainder.
More confident learners: Ask these children to make up two problems of their own involving division and remainders. Invite them to swap their problems with a partner to solve.

Common misconceptions
Children cannot convert the 'remainder' after doing the division.
Refer the children to a relevant practical example, such as five bars of chocolate shared between four people. Point out that the answer is 1¼ and the ¼ is the remaining whole bar of chocolate shared by 4 (the denominator) and that they each have one quarter, so 1 is the numerator.

Probing questions
● How did you decide whether to round up or down?
● What is 7 divided by 4?
● How may halves in 3½?

Next steps
Support: Give further examples of quotients as fractions. Encourage children to find, for example, how many sixths there are in 3½. When children are secure with quotients as fractions, ask them to give quotients as decimals. Refer back to Year 6 Block E Unit 1.
Extension: Give children further examples of real-life problems involving quotients. Invite them to think up some more examples of their own. Refer also to the Year 6 extension or Year 7 material if appropriate.

BLOCK E

Activity ⑩

Prior learning
Children can recognise equivalent fractions. They can identify the relationship between fractions, decimals and percentages.

Framework objective
Express one quantity as a percentage of another (for example, express £400 as a percentage of £1000); find equivalent percentages, decimals and fractions

Vocabulary
criteria, decimal, explain, fraction, multiple, percentage, predict, reason, reasoning, strategy

Resources
Display page: Which group?
Resource sheet: Self-assessment
Classroom resources: individual whiteboards and pens

⑩ Which group?

This activity should be done in small groups with the teacher or teaching assistant. Reveal the display page 'Which group?' on the whiteboard. Ask the children to sort these numbers into two groups. Discuss, as a group, what criteria could be used to sort the numbers ('equivalents of $^3/_{10}$' and 'equivalents of $^{14}/_{10}$'). As the children select the numbers to go into each group, ask them to explain their reasoning. When they have sorted all the numbers into the relevant groups, ask them to think of another fraction that could go into each group and to explain why. Decide whether to use the self-assessment sheet for the children to record their achievements and what they need to do next.

Teacher support
Less confident learners: This group could be given criteria for sorting the numbers before leading into the discussion.
More confident learners: Ask these children to suggest further numbers that could be added to the two groups. Encourage them to attempt to refine the criteria further.

Common misconceptions
Children do not recognise the relationship between fractions and percentages. Remind the children that *per cent* means 'parts per hundred'. Point out that 50 per cent is $^{50}/_{100}$, which is 0.50.

Probing questions
- What did you use as your sorting criteria?
- Can all the numbers be sorted using those criteria?
- How many equivalent fractions are there?

Next steps
Support: Give further practice at relating decimals to percentages, and then decimals to fractions, and also with finding equivalent fractions. Refer back to Year 6 Block E Unit 1.
Extension: Let this group work in pairs or small groups. One child suggests a decimal, fraction or percentage and the others identify equivalents. Refer also to the Year 6 extension or Year 7 material if appropriate.

BLOCK E

Activity ⑪

Prior learning Children understand the concept of 'scale'.	**Framework objective** Solve simple problems involving direct proportion by scaling quantities up or down **Vocabulary** pattern, proportion, ratio, scale, in every, for every, to every **Resources** **Worksheet:** Scale up

⑪ Scale up

Hand out copies of the worksheet 'Scale up'. Ask the children to work independently to solve the problems involving maps and plans that need scaling up or down, depending on a scale given as a ratio.

Teacher support
Less confident learners: Before these children start the activity, read through the worksheet with them and explain any problem areas.
More confident learners: Ask these children to think about other scales. For example, if the map had the scale 2cm to 5km, what would the measurements be on the map? Encourage them to try their ideas out with their partners.

Common misconceptions
Children are confused when changing the proportions of a two-dimensional shape.
Give the children the example of a square measuring 1cm × 1cm. Demonstrate that if the side length of the square is doubled, the area becomes four times greater. Remind the children that there are two dimensions to consider.

Probing questions
● If the scale is 1cm to 50km, what distance does 3cm represent?
● What is the relationship between the increase in the linear dimension and the increase in the area?

Next steps
Support: Give children simple maps to work with and ask them to measure distances. Help them to use the scale to work out the true distances. Refer back to Year 6 Block E Unit 1.
Extension: Give the children simple designs to enlarge, or allow them to draw their own designs and then enlarge them to a given scale. Refer also to the Year 6 extension or Year 7 material if appropriate.

Units 1, 2 & 3 📖 Periodic assessment

These activities can be used at any time during the teaching of this block to assess those children that you think have achieved the objective. A grid highlighting the related assessment focuses and expected learning outcomes for each activity can be found on the CD-ROM.

Decimal bingo

Framework objective
Use knowledge of place value and multiplication facts to 10 × 10 to derive related multiplication and division facts involving decimals

Learning outcome
● I can use place value and my tables to work out multiplication and division facts for decimals.

This activity should be carried out in small groups. Provide each child with a copy of the worksheet 'My bingo card'. Ask them to fill in 15 decimal numbers in the range 0.1 to 9.9 on the blank grid. Call out multiplication and division calculations with answers within this range (choose calculations such as 0.4 × 6; 5 × 0.8; 9.6 ÷ 3). Tell the children to cross out the answer if it is on their bingo card. When they have completed this activity, decide whether to use the self-assessment sheet for the children to record their achievements and next steps.

Show it

Framework objective
Use efficient written methods to add and subtract integers and decimals, to multiply and divide integers and decimals by a one-digit integer, and to multiply two-digit and three-digit integers by a two-digit integer

Learning outcome
● I can use efficient written methods to add, subtract, multiply and divide whole numbers and decimals.

Give each child a copy of the worksheet 'Show it'. Ask them to work out the calculations using a written method and to record their methods fully.

Credit crunch

Framework objective
Express one quantity as a percentage of another; find equivalent percentages, decimals and fractions

Learning outcome
● I can work out a quantity as a percentage of another and find equivalent percentages, decimals and fractions.

Provide each child with a copy of the worksheet 'Credit crunch'. Ask the children to work out the different costs for the items after discount. Remind them to read the questions carefully before filling in the answers.

Name	Date

Show it

◼ Work out these calculations using a full written method.

◼ Show all your workings.

1. 3687 – 1928	**2.** 3459 + 478
3. 35.6 + 78.9 + 30.65	**4.** 76.3 – 16.9
5. 38.5 ÷ 7	**6.** 234.6 × 8
7. 36 × 98	**8.** 621 × 47

How easy?

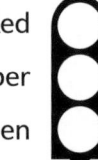

Red

Amber

Green

How do you think you have done?

_____

_____

PHOTOCOPIABLE ■ SCHOLASTIC

Name	Date

Credit crunch

Mrs Brown needs a new cooker. She has been looking at the different offers and is confused. Help her to find the best deal.

◀ Budget Stores has a cooker on offer for £575, but will give a 40% discount for cash. How much will it cost?

_____

◀ Superstore has the same cooker on sale for £625, but will give a 45% discount. How much will it cost?

_____

◀ Where should she buy her new cooker?

_____

◀ Mrs Brown also sees the new fridge that she wants in Budget Stores. This is priced at £280 but her husband says it is only $\frac{3}{5}$ of that price in Electro Discounts.

◀ Should she buy it at Budget Stores with their 40% discount or should she buy at Electro Discounts?

_____

How easy?

Red ◯
Amber ◯
Green ◯

How do you think you have done?

_____

_____

BLOCK E

Transitional assessment

Activity	Type	Level	Description
3.1a 3.1b	Single-level written assessments	3	Two 20-minute formal test papers covering objectives from all Strands of the Framework at Level 3 (one calculator, one non-calculator)
3.2a 3.2b	Single-level written assessment	3	Two 20-minute formal test papers covering objectives from all Strands of the Framework at Level 3 (one calculator, one non-calculator)
3.3a 3.3b	Single-level written assessment	3	Two 20-minute formal test papers covering objectives from all Strands of the Framework at Level 3 (one calculator, one non-calculator)
3.4	Single-level oral assessment	3	Approximately 5-minute oral paper covering objectives from all Strands of the Framework at Level 3
3.5	Single-level oral assessment	3	Approximately 5-minute oral paper covering objectives from all Strands of the Framework at Level 3
4.1a 4.1b	Single-level written assessments	4	Two 20-minute formal test papers covering objectives from all Strands of the Framework at Level 4 (one calculator, one non-calculator)
4.2a 4.2b	Single-level written assessment	4	Two 20-minute formal test papers covering objectives from all Strands of the Framework at Level 4 (one calculator, one non-calculator)
4.3a 4.3b	Single-level written assessment	4	Two 20-minute formal test papers covering objectives from all Strands of the Framework at Level 4 (one calculator, one non-calculator)
4.4	Single-level oral assessment	4	Approximately 5-minute oral paper covering objectives from all Strands of the Framework at Level 4
4.5	Single-level oral assessment	4	Approximately 5-minute oral paper covering objectives from all Strands of the Framework at Level 4
5.1a 5.1b	Single-level written assessments	5	Two 20-minute formal test papers covering objectives from all Strands of the Framework at Level 5 (one calculator, one non-calculator)
5.2a 5.2b	Single-level written assessment	5	Two 20-minute formal test papers covering objectives from all Strands of the Framework at Level 5 (one calculator, one non-calculator)
5.3a 5.3b	Single-level written assessment	5	Two 20-minute formal test papers covering objectives from all Strands of the Framework at Level 5 (one calculator, one non-calculator)
5.4	Single-level oral assessment	5	Approximately 5-minute oral paper covering objectives from all Strands of the Framework at Level 5
5.5	Single-level oral assessment	5	Approximately 5-minute oral paper covering objectives from all Strands of the Framework at Level 5

Written test instructions

Allow 20 minutes for each paper.
Children should work so that they cannot see each other's work.
Do not explain questions or read numbers to the children.
Teachers may choose to read the questions aloud to children, if they feel it is appropriate.
The test may be administered to groups of children or to the whole class.
The total marks available for each paper is given in the mark scheme.

Say to children:
Here are some questions (I am going to read some questions) for you to answer.
For some questions you will write your answer in a box. [Show example.]
For some questions you may need to draw lines or rings to show your answer.
[Show example.]
If you make a mistake, you should cross it out (or rub it out neatly) and write your answer clearly.
You may use spaces on the paper to do any working out that may help you.
Try to work out the answer to each question before going on to the next one.
If you can't answer a question, move on to the next one - it may be easier.

Equipment for each child
pencil, eraser (or children may cross out mistakes), 30cm ruler (marked in mm), mirror, tracing paper, protractor

Oral test instructions

Read questions to the children no more than twice.
Allow time allocated on each paper for each question: 5, 10 or 15 seconds.
Children record their answers on paper.
1 mark per question: 15 or 20 marks in total

Equipment for each child
pencil, eraser (or children may cross out mistakes), 30cm ruler
Separate teacher resources are listed for on each paper.

Levelling the children

Add together the marks from an oral test and a combined mark for both written tests A and B.

Level 3		Level 4		Level 5	
Below Level 3	0 – 21 marks	Below Level 4	0 – 21 marks	Below Level 5	0 – 21 marks
Low Level 3	22 – 31 marks	Low Level 4	22 – 31 marks	Low Level 5	22 – 31 marks
Secure Level 3	32 – 40 marks	Secure Level 4	32 – 40 marks	Secure Level 5	32 – 40 marks
High Level 3	40 - 50 marks	High Level 4	40 – 50 marks	High Level 5	40 – 50 marks

When awarding an end-of-year Teacher Assessment Level, teachers also need to consider a child's performance on Periodic and Day-to-Day Assessments.

TRANSITIONAL

Mathematics: making a level judgement

Use these steps to formalise your assessments of pupils' mathematics into level judgements.

You will need
- evidence of the pupil's mathematics that shows most independence, for example from work in other subjects as well as in mathematics lessons
- other evidence of the pupil as a mathematician, for example notes on plans, the pupil's own reflections, your own recollections of classroom interactions, oral answers given during mental starters
- a copy of the assessment guidelines for the level borderline that is your starting point.

Step 1: Making best fit judgements
Within each assessment focus, draw on the pupil's work and other evidence including what you know about the pupil's mathematics. Use the criteria in the assessment guidelines to decide which level provides the best fit.

Step 2: Work through Ma2 Number
Begin with the assessment guidelines for Ma2 Number.

Look at the criteria within each AF. Decide which level describes the pupil best.

Record the level for each AF in the appropriate box.

Record 'insufficient evidence' (IE) if you do not know enough about this aspect of the pupil's mathematics to make a judgement. This has implications for planning.

If you feel the pupil is operating below the level, check the criteria on the assessment guidelines for the level below.

Step 3: Making an overall level judgement for Ma2 Number
Now make your level decision for Ma2 Number.

- Your AF judgements give an impression of the best fit level for Ma2.
- Read the complete level descriptions for both levels to confirm your impression of the best fit level for Ma2

Decide whether the level is Low, Secure or High. Do this by thinking about what the pupil demonstrates ie:
- how much of the level
- how consistently
- how independently
- in what range of contexts.

Tick the relevant Low, Secure or High box for the level.

Step 4 Repeat the process for Ma3, Ma4 and then Ma1
For the Ma1 judgement, consider how the pupil uses and applies the mathematics of Ma2, Ma3 and Ma4.

APP ☐ Self-assessment sheet

Name	Date

Activity name _____

Objective:
Learning outcome:
Comments:

Self-assessment

How well did you do this? _____

_____

_____

_____

What do you still need to do? _____

_____

_____

_____

How easy?

Red

Amber

Green

How do you think you have done?

_____

_____